Drug Misuse

ISSUES
(formerly Issues for the Nineties)

Volume 2

Editor

Craig Donnellan

Independence

Educational Publishers
Cambridge

First published by Independence
PO Box 295
Cambridge CB1 3XP
England

British Library Cataloguing in Publication Data
Drug Misuse – (Issues Series)
I. Donnellan, Craig II. Series
362.2'9'0941

ISBN 1 86168 164 X

Printed in Great Britain
The Burlington Press
Cambridge

Typeset by
Claire Boyd

Cover
The illustration on the front cover is by
Pumpkin House.

CONTENTS

Introduction

Drug Misuse is the second volume in the **Issues** series. The aim of this series is to offer up-to-date information about important issues in our world.

Drug Misuse looks at the different kinds of drugs, the effects and dangers of drug misuse, and also examines the legalisation debate.

The information comes from a wide variety of sources and includes:
Government reports and statistics
Newspaper reports and features
Magazine articles and surveys
Literature from lobby groups
and charitable organisations.

It is hoped that, as you read about the many aspects of the issues explored in this book, you will critically evaluate the information presented. It is important that you decide whether you are being presented with facts or opinions. Does the writer give a biased or an unbiased report? If an opinion is being expressed, do you agree with the writer?

Drug Misuse offers a useful starting-point for those who need convenient access to information about the many issues involved. However, it is only a starting-point. At the back of the book is a list of organisations which you may want to contact for further information.

*****

The facts of drugs

Information on drugs from the Health Education Board for Scotland (HEBS)

There are so many drugs around that it can all get a bit confusing but they can be grouped roughly into three main types:

Stimulants – these make everything seem as if it's going faster, including thoughts, speech and the body.

Depressants – these slow everything down, including thoughts, speech and the body.

Hallucinogens – these alter the way a person sees, hears and feels things, causing hallucinations and confusion.

These are the main drugs which fall into the above three categories:

Stimulants

MDMA, also known by a variety of street names such as the commonly-named Ecstasy or E; love hearts, doves, rhubarb and custard, and disco burger.

You've probably heard quite a lot about Ecstasy. It's quite a new drug but has quickly become popular with young people and is often in the news.

Ecstasy is sold in the form of white or brown tablets or capsules and because it's so new, the medical effects are not yet entirely clear.

Short-term effects: The effect of the drug comes on after 20 minutes to an hour and can last for several hours. The person who's taken it feels very energetic and carefree. One of the well-known dangers of Ecstasy is that it can cause the body to overheat. This can lead to heatstroke, dehydration and even death. It is important that if a person has taken the drug and is in a hot place and dances a lot, they drink plenty of water and take rests. However, drinking too much water can also be dangerous. A pint of water an hour combined with the occasional salty snack such as peanuts will help maintain the body's fluid and salt balance. Alcohol should be avoided as this causes dehydration.

Long-term effects: The research so far shows that if people use Ecstasy regularly they can become anxious and confused and their sleep patterns can become disturbed. There is also some evidence that it can cause liver damage or trigger epileptic fits. As you no doubt know, there have been a number of tragic deaths involving young people taking Ecstasy – these are most probably related to the overheating it causes, as mentioned above.

Amphetamine, known most commonly as speed, and also uppers, whizz, sulph or sulphate.
Amphetamine is most often sold as a white, or off white, powder in a specially folded scrap of paper.

Short-term effects: The person who's taken amphetamine feels more confident and has a lot more energy. They usually lose their appetite while they are taking amphetamine ('speeding'). They can feel very depressed when the 'high' wears off and if they take the drug often they can feel irritable and all on edge.

Long-term effects: The more somebody uses amphetamine, the more their body becomes used to it and they have to take more to get the same effect. If someone takes a large amount of amphetamine, there is a risk of their heart stopping under the strain. If they go on using amphetamine heavily for a long time, they run the risk of becoming mentally ill. This will improve if they stop taking the amphetamine but they might need to have specialist treatment and spend several months recovering. Recent evidence also suggests that amphetamine can cause liver damage.

Cocaine and crack, also known as coke, snow and base

Cocaine is sold as a white powder and is usually sniffed but can be smoked. Crack, a very powerful form of cocaine, comes as small crystals and is smoked – it's especially dangerous as people become dependent on it very quickly. Cocaine is expensive and is not widely used in Scotland. Thankfully, neither is crack.

Short-term effects: The effects are similar to amphetamine but stronger. The person who's taken it feels on top of the world. The effects also wear off more quickly and because it's more powerful the taker runs a higher risk of heart failure.

Long-term effects: Again, the effects on the mind and body if used regularly are similar to amphetamine. If someone uses the drug a lot and takes a great deal of it they can become dependent on it. Sniffing the powder can damage the inside of the nose and smoking crack may lead to breathing problems.

Amyl and butyl nitrites, also known as poppers

These are vapours which are inhaled through the mouth or nose. Amyl and butyl nitrites are controlled under the Medicines Act and its sale through clubs, bars and sex shops is illegal. There are no controls on the sale of butyl nitrites at present.

Short-term effects: The person who's inhaled these vapours feels a 'rushing' sensation as their blood vessels dilate. They may also cause headaches, vomiting and dermatitis. If a lot is inhaled there can be severe vomiting, the body can go into dangerous shock, and the person can become unconscious – there have been deaths associated with amyl nitrite.

Long-term effects: The person who uses it regularly can find they become tolerant and therefore might inhale more, running the risk of the dangers above.

Depressants

Heroin, also known as junk, smack, brown, scag and H

Heroin comes as light brown powder. Very occasionally it might be white.

It can be injected, sniffed or smoked. It's when people inject it that it's most dangerous because they also run the risk of getting HIV – the virus which leads to AIDS – from shared injecting equipment, and because they can't be sure what other substances might have been mixed with the heroin before it was sold. Sharing injecting equipment with any drug is a risk for HIV and the person can often get other serious infections which can include blood poisoning and serious liver disease. Recently there have been reports of young people smoking heroin. This may make it seem more acceptable to young people by taking away the barriers associated with injecting. But heroin is highly addictive and dangerous whichever way it is taken.

Short-term effects: Heroin slows down the brain and also the things that the body normally does naturally, like coughing and breathing. The rate the heart beats at is also slowed down. The person who's taken heroin can feel drowsy and free from worry and pain. There's a risk of overdose as it's difficult to know how pure or strong the heroin is and this can lead to the person falling unconscious and dying because of an overdose. If heroin is used at the same time as other drugs which slow down the body, there is also an increased risk of the person overdosing.

Long-term effects: If a person uses heroin their body and mind get used to the drug and they need to take more – they become dependent on the drug to feel normal, never mind

experience the pleasurable effects. If someone who's become dependent on heroin stops taking the drug, their body 'withdraws' from it and they experience severe physical and mental symptoms.

Tranquillisers, also known as tranx, benzos, eggs, jellies and norries

Tranquillisers such as diazepam (Valium), chlordiazepoxide (Librium), lorazepam (Ativan) and temazepam are often prescribed by doctors for people who are having difficulty sleeping or feeling very anxious. They come as tablets or capsules. Used as directed they shouldn't cause too many problems although some people who have been legally prescribed these drugs do become dependent on them after long-term use and have great difficulty when they try to stop using them. Tranquillisers become more dangerous when they're used as a recreational drug as the person might mix them with alcohol or inject them. This is a particular problem with temazepam.

Short-term effects: Tranquillisers have a calming effect, and stop people feeling anxious. There is a danger that people might overdose on them if they take too much or drink alcohol at the same time. Temazepam injected from dissolved gelatine capsules – 'jellies' – has caused particular problems as they can re-solidify in the body and cause very serious problems such as abscesses, thrombosis and even gangrene. Injecting also carries a high risk of HIV and other serious infections if injecting equipment is shared.

Long-term effects: People who take tranquillisers for more than a few months can become dependent on them. They can also become depressed and aggressive and their behaviour can become unpredictable. When someone tries to stop taking tranquillisers they can 'withdraw' and experience unpleasant symptoms like restlessness and anxiety.

Methadone

Methadone is used to treat people who've become dependent on opiates like heroin. It is taken orally. It comes as a green or yellowish liquid. Methadone is also occasionally misused and is often injected.

Short-term effects: The person who has taken methadone feels quite like someone who's taken heroin but the effect is less intense and lasts longer. It can make the person feel in control of their emotions and soothed, but although it causes drowsiness the person has difficulty sleeping. It sometimes makes people feel sick too.

Long-term effects: Methadone is a powerful drug. Just 10mg is enough to kill a child, a few mouthfuls is enough to kill a teenager, and less than 50mg could kill an adult who isn't used to the drug. It leads to the body needing the drug as well as the person feeling dependent on it – if the person tries to stop taking it, they have withdrawal symptoms.

Volatile substances, including solvents

The big problem with volatile substances is that they are so easily available. Lots of things you might normally keep in the house, such as solvent-based glues, lighter fuel, cleaning agents and aerosols, have been inhaled by young people trying to get high. In Scotland, under Common Law, retailers can be prosecuted for knowingly supplying volatile substances which they suspect will be abused. Volatile substance abuse is also grounds for referral to the Children's Panel.

Short-term effects: Depending on which substance is inhaled, the effects can last anything from a few minutes to half an hour. Some of the effects of sniffing solvents are similar to alcohol and the person can feel very high. Other people may hallucinate. This means of course that, like people who've been drinking, they're much more likely to be involved in or cause an accident. The effects are also more unpredictable than alcohol as you can't be sure of the strength and exact effect of each substance.

There are some very serious dangers with solvents such as the risk of suffocation when plastic bags are held over the face when inhaling to concentrate the effects of the substance. Some solvents also make the person feel sick and they can choke on their own vomit. When a person inhales from an aerosol there is also the risk of sudden suffocation or their heart stopping.

Long-term effects: If a person inhales solvents regularly, they can find that their memory is affected and they find it difficult to concentrate. You should also remember never to chase after anyone you catch sniffing solvents because violent exercise after sniffing can lead to the heart suddenly stopping beating.

Hallucinogens
Lysergic acid diethylamide (LSD), also known as acid and trips

Acid is normally sold in small amounts which have been soaked into blotting paper printed with various designs. When a person takes it, they have hallucinations. The way they see, hear and feel the world around them changes both at the time of taking the drug and in the form of 'flashbacks' afterwards.

Short-term effects: The effect produced by acid is called a 'trip' and the person usually starts tripping within about an hour of taking it. It can take up to 12 hours for it to wear off. The person might see bright colours, hear strange sounds or, more extremely, see weird visions or have weird thoughts. If someone is seeing and hearing things which simply aren't there they are likely to behave in ways which are a danger to themselves and others. The experience can vary a lot – a 'good trip' or a 'bad trip' – depending on what the person feels like and what they see, feel or hear when the drug is affecting them.

Long-term effects: There is no evidence of long-term damage to the body and little evidence of long-term change or damage to personality or behaviour. But the person can have 'flashbacks' when they might re-experience the 'trip' without having taken the drug again.

Cannabis, also known as dope, draw, shit, smoke, grass, and hash

Grass is the dried leaves of the cannabis plant and the other names refer to the resin or oil. It is usually mixed with tobacco and smoked in a 'joint' or 'spliff', but is also smoked without tobacco in pipes. A new variety of cannabis called 'skunk' has appeared recently which has been specially grown for strength.

Short-term effects: Cannabis makes the person feel relaxed and because it's a mild hallucinogen, they can find colours and sounds brighter and sharper. It can, however, cause anxiety, affect short-term memory and because the person is high, make them less able to carry out complicated tasks.

Long-term effects: If a person smokes regularly or very heavily, they could have heart, lung and breathing problems, as with cigarettes. They might also feel depressed and restless and anyone who has any mental problems should not smoke cannabis regularly.

Magic mushrooms, also known as mushies

These mushrooms grow wild throughout Scotland and are usually collected in the autumn. They are mostly dried and eaten or sometimes diluted with water to make 'mushroom tea'.

Short-term effects: Magic mushrooms have similar dangers to LSD but the effects are not as strong. The extra danger with these mushrooms is picking a poisonous mushroom by mistake and eating it.

Long-term effects: There are no serious long-term effects known.

• The above information is an extract from the booklet *The Facts of Drugs – a Parent's Guide*, produced by the Health Education Board for Scotland (HEBS). See page 41 for address details.
© *Health Education Board for Scotland (HEBS)*

Cannabis

Information from the Libra Project

Cannabis

Other names: Spliff, Grass, Weed, Marijuana, Dope, Ganja, Hash(ish), Smoke, Joint, Pot, Puff, Blow.

How is it taken ?

Cannabis can be smoked (on its own or with tobacco) or eaten. Cannabis oil is sometimes used, which is simply spread on a normal cigarette, but by far the most common form of cannabis used is cannabis resin. This comes in a variety of forms (for example a flat press) and is usually chocolate brown in colour with a hard consistency. The resin is heated (to soften it) and then a small amount is mixed with tobacco and rolled into a cigarette. If the dried leaves and buds are used ('grass') then this is often smoked on its own, without using tobacco. Cannabis can also be smoked through a pipe or a bong (a pipe in which the smoke is pulled through water first to cool it down). Pipes are often home-made, using whatever equipment is available. If cannabis is eaten the effects can often be confusing – it is usually between 5 and 10 minutes before the effects of the drug can be felt when smoking, but up to an hour or more when eaten. Sometimes the user can suddenly find themselves more 'stoned' than they had expected, and may panic. Once eaten, the amount of cannabis consumed cannot be regulated as it can when smoking.

What happens?

A lot depends upon the user's mental state before smoking, the environment and the user's expectations. Cannabis causes perceptual changes which make the user more aware of other people's feelings, enhance the enjoyment of music and give a general feeling of euphoria. It can also make the user feel agitated if they are in a situation which is not pleasant – if they are with strangers or trying to hide the fact that they are using – which is often referred to as a paranoia. In extreme moments, the user can feel that everything said around them is directed at them in a malicious and hurtful way. Using cannabis with other drugs such as alcohol can make the user feel dizzy and disoriented. A change of environment – turning the music off, having a glass of water, turning a light on or having a breath of fresh air – will often make you feel better quickly. If you're feeling low, using cannabis will not make you feel better. It is more likely that you will sit and think about what is going on than forget about it.

Physical changes

Cannabis causes a number of physical changes – these are the things that any commercial drug based around THC is trying to isolate. It can produce an increased pulse rate, a decrease in blood pressure, the alleviation of excess pressure in the eye, an opening of the airway leading to the lungs and suppression of the vomit reflex. It can also produce bloodshot eyes, dry mouth, dizziness and an increased appetite. Sometimes short-term memory loss (i.e. the last couple of minutes) can occur, although this passes as the effects of the drug wear off. To fatally overdose on cannabis it is estimated

that you would need to eat about one and a half pounds of resin in one sitting. Cannabis is not physically addictive.

Keeping safe

Whether cannabis use leads to long-term health problems or not is unknown. There has been little research in this country, and research undertaken in other countries is clearly affected by other environmental factors, hence inconclusive. If cannabis is smoked regularly, then respiratory complaints similar to those linked with cigarette smoking are likely to occur. If a cannabis user does have an unpleasant experience when using the drug it is often the result of a high dose coupled with inexperience – perhaps after eating a large amount (i.e. more than a sixteenth of an ounce) and then panicking when the drug takes effect, or when cannabis is used with another drug such as alcohol. Cannabis is fat soluble, and so someone who regularly uses a large amount of the drug may store some of it in their body. It can take up to thirty days for this to be fully metabolised and for the body to be clear of the drug. Cannabis is a hallucinogen. Hallucinogens have been linked to mental health problems – the hallucinogenic experience may trigger a psychotic episode for someone with a pre-existing mental health condition (which they may or may not know about). Someone using cannabis may experience occasional paranoia (best described as irrational fear) whilst intoxicated, particularly likely if they feel unsafe (using the drug with people they don't know or mistrust, for example). There has been a lot of discussion about the potentially beneficial medical uses of this substance, and its place in modern medicine. However, there is still little research into new cannabis-based products because of the difficulties in obtaining research licences and the political issues around the legalisation of cannabis.

Legal status

Cannabis is illegal. Cannabis plants and resin are Class B drugs in the Misuse of Drugs Act 1971, whilst cannabis oil is a Class A drug. Cannabis is a schedule 1 drug, meaning that it is considered to have no legitimate therapeutic use. Other Class B drugs are amphetamines and barbiturates. If found guilty of possession of a Class B drug for personal use and sentenced in a magistrate's court, the offence carries a maximum sentence of three months' imprisonment and a fine of two thousand five hundred pounds. Generally a simple possession offence relating to cannabis will result in a fine only. The maximum sentence for supplying the drug if tried at a magistrate's court is six months imprisonment and a fine of two thousand pounds. If found guilty of simple possession of a Class B drug and sentenced at Crown Court, the offence carries a maximum sentence of five years' imprisonment and an unlimited fine. A charge of possession of a drug with intent to supply can be brought by the police. This includes giving a substance away for free, and can be for any amount of cannabis that the court feels is too unreasonably large to be for personal use only. An ounce of cannabis in eight separate blocks may be seen by a court as intent to supply, as if it were for personal use there would be no need to cut it up. Dealing in larger amounts of cannabis can lead to a charge of trafficking. At Crown Court a maximum sentence of 14 years' imprisonment and an unlimited fine could be imposed for this offence. If you are searched, questioned or arrested by the police and are not sure of your rights, the charity RELEASE are available 24 hours a day to advise you. Their helpline number is (020) 7603 8654, and you can ask the Desk Sergeant to contact them for you if you are taken to a Police Station. It is wise to exercise your right to silence until you have spoken to them or a solicitor.

© Libra Project

Solvents

Information from Release

What are solvents?

The term solvents is used to describe a wide variety of everyday substances such as aerosols, glues, fire extinguisher fluids, nail varnish remover, paint, petrol and dozens more. They contain chemicals that can alter our state of mind for a short time. Solvents also include such volatile substances as butane gas and propane.

How are they taken?

Solvents are usually breathed in or sniffed. This means that they take effect quickly because the substances go directly from the lungs into the bloodstream.

What are the effects?

The effects of sniffing are similar to those of alcohol and may bring on light-headedness, giddiness and a sense of adventure. The longer you sniff at any one time, the stronger the effects are likely to be and so you may soon feel out of control, confused or drowsy. Some people experience hallucinations – seeing or hearing imaginary things – but this is rare. The effects of sniffing don't usually last longer than half an hour.

What are the side-effects?

Side-effects can include headaches and sickness. With repeated use of glue, the skin around the mouth and nose can become irritated, resulting in a rash, and you may feel depressed. These should all disappear as you take less or stop altogether.

What are the dangers?

Like many substances, what you sniff may be made up of a mixture of chemicals, making it difficult to know exactly what's in them. Any interruption of breathing is the biggest risk and in some cases has resulted in death. This can be caused by sniffing too much in an enclosed space so you don't get enough air, or sniffing until you become unconscious. Using butane gas or aerosols is particularly dangerous. When sprayed directly into the mouth the throat is cooled, which can result in breathing difficulties or suffocation.

As with alcohol, accidents can happen when under the influence of solvents because you have less control over your body. Because of this, the places used for sniffing can be the main danger, for example:
- too isolated and out of reach of medical help
- high up (e.g. in a tree/on a wall)
- near water (e.g. canal bank)

Using butane gas and petrol is particularly dangerous and both are inflammable, increasing the risk of fire. Some solvents can cause the heart to be more sensitive to adrenalin, a substance produced by vigorous exercise such as running or fear. In a few cases this has resulted in death.

Solvents aren't physically addictive. If you sniff regularly, you may feel that you can't do without it for a while after you've cut down or stopped. These cravings will lessen with time.

What is the legal position?

It's not illegal to take or possess solvents, but under the Intoxicating Substances Supply Act 1985, it's an offence to supply to a young person under 18 a substance which the supplier knows, or has reason to believe, will be used 'to achieve intoxication'.

- The above information is from Release's web site which can be found at www.release.org.uk

© Reproduced by kind permission of Release Publications Ltd.

Drug use among children rises to 11%

Government survey of 11- to 15-year-olds finds warnings ignored

By Patrick Wintour, Chief Political Correspondent

Drug misuse among school children is on the increase, with the number admitting using drugs up from 10% to 11%, according to a government survey published yesterday. Nearly two-thirds of 15-year-olds said they had been offered drugs in the past year.

The findings, which run counter to recent claims that progress is being made in the fight against drugs, showed that more than one in 10 children aged 11-15 used drugs over the past 12 months, and suggested that government efforts to stem the flow of drugs are failing.

At the same time, the number of regular cigarette smokers was found to be on a relatively sharp decline, especially among boys, a trend that started in the mid-1980s.

Most school drug users said they had been using cannabis. Surprisingly, the greatest use had been among children in relatively affluent neighbourhoods. Users tended to be children with low expectations of good exam results and generally low esteem. The survey also found that children were eight times more likely to take drugs if their brothers or sisters did so.

'The general picture is a fairly consistent one of small increases amongst both boys and girls, particularly amongst those aged 14 and 15,' said the authors.

The survey, which was conducted among more than 9,000 secondary school children aged 11-15 in some 340 schools in England, is the largest of its kind and is seen as more revealing than simple crime figures showing the number of children cautioned for possessing or selling cannabis.

The government's anti-drugs co-ordinator, Keith Hellawell, yesterday chose to ignore the increase, instead praising the common sense of the majority of teenagers who had not taken drugs.

The survey showed that boys were more likely to take drugs than girls, by 13% to 12%. But there was a growing likelihood of drug taking as children grew older.

> *One child in every 100 had tried drugs before their 11th birthday. By the age of 16, 39% of children have tried drugs, according to the survey – which also predicted that that figure would rise*

As many as 30% of 15-year-olds had taken drugs in the previous year, but only 1% of 11-year-olds. Asian British youngsters were proportionately more unlikely to take drugs, with only 7% admitting having taken drugs in the previous year, against 12% of pupils described as white.

A sense of failure at school seemed to be likely to lead children to drugs, with 30% of those that said they were not doing well at school taking drugs. Drug misuse was heavily associated with other forms of anti-social behaviour, with drug users four times more likely to steal, and truants and those excluded from school five times more likely to take drugs.

Three-quarters of drug users said they had not told their parents. Yet even among those who did tell their parents, only half thought their parents disapproved. Brothers or sisters or close friends taking drugs was a key determinant.

Ministers can take some solace from the finding that there is no sign that drug education programmes in schools actually increase the likelihood of children taking drugs. However, other messages from the government do not seem to be getting through. Most pupils said they enjoyed the experience, 70% saying they had felt 'high, fantastic, happy or giggly'.

One child in every 100 had tried drugs before their 11th birthday. By the age of 16, 39% of children have tried drugs, according to the survey – which also predicted that that figure would rise; 55% have smoked cigarettes; and 73% have had an alcoholic drink.

Mr Hellawell said: 'Children nowadays have to be told of the full dangers of drugs and have the details spelled out so that they clearly understand the dangers. They are young adults; advising "just say no", which has never been our policy, does not recognise the need for the kind of structured anti-drugs education programmes the government has in place.'

He said 93% of secondary and 75% of primary schools now had a drugs education policy – up from 86% of secondary and 61% of primary schools in 1997.

The state of the drugs problem in the European Union

Information from the European Monitoring Centre for Drugs and Drug Addiction

Trends in drug use and its consequences

Cannabis

Cannabis remains the most widely available and commonly used drug across the EU, with substantial increases in use over the 1990s. Continuing rises in countries with previously lower levels and some stabilisation in higher-prevalence countries confirm the tendency towards convergence noted last year.

- At least 45 million Europeans (18% of those aged 15 to 64) have tried cannabis at least once. Around 15 million (about 6% of those aged 15 to 64) have used cannabis in the past 12 months.
- Use is higher among younger age groups. About 25% of those aged 15 to 16 and 40% of those aged 18 have tried cannabis. In some countries, use has doubled since 1990, in others the rise is less marked and in a few it has stabilised.
- 'Curiosity' is a primary motive for trying cannabis, and use is more experimental or intermittent than persistent.
- The increase in numbers attending treatment centres for cannabis use noted last year is confirmed, especially among younger clients. Additional drugs are also often involved.
- Cannabis remains the primary drug in drug offences, mostly for use or possession rather than trafficking. Numbers of seizures have increased sharply since 1997.

Amphetamines and ecstasy

Amphetamines and ecstasy are the second most commonly used drugs in Europe. Following increases in the 1990s, ecstasy use appears to be stabilising or even falling, while amphetamine use is stable or rising.

- Between 1 and 5% of those aged 16 to 34 have taken amphetamines and/or ecstasy. Rates are higher in narrower age groups, but rarely exceed 10%.
- The proportion of clients seeking treatment for amphetamine or other stimulant use is low, but increasing in some countries.
- Drug use continues to shift away from large dance events to more geographically diffuse club, bar and private settings.
- A wider range of drugs and patterns of use are observed, linked to different social groups and lifestyles.
- Both the numbers and quantities of amphetamine seizures stabilised in 1998. Ecstasy seizures have been stable since 1997, although the quantities involved fluctuate.

Cocaine

While cocaine is less commonly used than amphetamines or ecstasy, its use is rising – particularly among socially active groups – and spreading to a broader population.

- Between 1 and 6% of those aged 16 to 34 and 1 to 2% of schoolchildren have tried cocaine at least once, although some surveys show levels of up to 4% among 15- to 16-year-olds.
- Higher levels of use are found among socially outgoing, employed young adults in urban centres.
- Cocaine tends to be used experimentally or intermittently and is usually sniffed in powder form.
- Many clients treated for heroin use also use cocaine either

How Europe compares

Percentage of 15- to 16-year-olds who have used any type of illicit drugs in their lifetime (1999)		Percentage of 15- to 16-year-olds who reported daily smoking at the age of 13 or younger (1999)		Percentage of 15- to 16-year-olds who have been drunk 20 times or more in a lifetime (1999)	
UK	36	UK	20	Denmark	41
Ireland	32	Ireland	18	UK	29
Italy	26	Moscow	16	Ireland	25
Denmark	25	Finland	15	Finland	28
Poland	18	France	14	Sweden	19
Iceland	16	Denmark	12	Norway	16
Norway	13	Norway	11	Poland	11
Portugal	12	Sweden	10	Moscow	10
Finland	10	Portugal	8	France	4
Sweden	9	Italy	6	Greece	4
Malta	8	Cyprus	5	Portugal	4
Cyprus	3	Greece	3	Cyprus	2

Source: The European School Survey Project on Alcohol and Other Drugs (ESPAD)

intravenously or smoked as 'crack'.

- Severe problems associated with smoking 'crack' have been identified, particularly among female sex workers.
- The proportion of clients seeking treatment for cocaine use is increasing in many countries. How far this is linked to heroin use or has developed from heavy recreational use of other drugs is unclear.
- In 1998, numbers of cocaine seizures continued to increase, while the quantities involved fluctuated.

Heroin

Heroin dependence remains broadly stable. Known users are a largely ageing population with serious health, social and psychiatric problems, although indications of heroin use amongst some younger groups are noted.

- Heroin experience overall remains low (1 to 2% in young adults) and school surveys show pupils are highly cautious about using heroin.
- Some countries report anecdotal evidence of increased heroin smoking among young people, and some school surveys reveal greater experimentation.
- Heroin use is reported amongst young, heavy, 'recreational' users of amphetamines, ecstasy and other drugs. Other high-risk groups include marginalised minorities, homeless young people, institutionalised youth and young offenders, prisoners (women in particular) and sex workers.
- New clients entering treatment for heroin use are less likely to inject and more likely to smoke the drug than clients returning to treatment.
- Numbers of heroin seizures and the quantities involved are stable across the EU, although variations exist between countries.

Multiple drug use

Patterns of weekend and 'recreational' drug use increasingly involve combinations of illicit and licit drugs, including alcohol and tranquillisers.

- 'Nightlife' studies reveal heavy multiple drug use by a minority of young people.
- Use of synthetic drugs such as ketamine and gamma hydroxy-butyrate (GHB) is reported, but is much less common than use of amphetamines or ecstasy.
- More significant is the increase in cocaine use, often in conjunction with heavy alcohol consumption.
- Abuse of volatile substances (lighter fuel, aerosols, glue) is often more common amongst schoolchildren than amphetamines and ecstasy, and is increasing in some countries.

Problem drug use and demand for treatment

Patterns of problem drug use – often characterised as 'addiction', especially to heroin – are changing across the EU. In addition to heroin dependence, problem use of cocaine (often with alcohol), multiple use of drugs such as amphetamines, ecstasy and medicines, and heavy cannabis use are emerging.

- The EU has an estimated 1.5 million problem drug – mainly heroin – users (between two and seven per 1,000 inhabitants aged 15 to 64). An estimated 1 million are likely to meet clinical criteria for dependence.
- The proportion of clients entering treatment for heroin use is generally declining, while new admissions for cocaine or cannabis use show some increases – especially among young clients.

Drug-related deaths

The number of acute drug-related deaths (overdoses or poisonings) has stabilised across the EU following marked increases in the second half of the 1980s and early

1990s. Trends vary, however, among countries.

- Stable or decreasing rates may be linked to stable or decreasing prevalence of heroin, safer usage or increased access to treatment, especially substitution programmes.
- Countries with previously low numbers of acute deaths directly linked to drug administration ('overdoses') report substantial rises in recent years. This may reflect increased prevalence of problem drug use, but also improved recording practices.
- Other countries continue to report less sharp, but steady increases in acute deaths.
- Numbers of drug-related deaths are significantly higher among men than women, reflecting the higher prevalence of problem drug use in males.
- Most acute deaths involve opiates, often in combination with alcohol or tranquillisers. Some countries report significant numbers of deaths from volatile substances among adolescents. Deaths from cocaine, amphetamines or ecstasy are uncommon.
- Overall annual mortality among problem drug users has fallen in some countries, following rises over several years. This reflects a drop in overdose and AIDS deaths and indicates that some deaths are preventable.

Drug-related infectious diseases

Overall trends in HIV and hepatitis B and C prevalence among injecting drug users appear relatively stable, although some local increases in HIV infection are reported.

- Incidence of new AIDS cases varies greatly between countries, but generally continues to fall, probably because of new treatments that delay onset.
- Prevalence of hepatitis C infection among drug injectors is high – between 50 and 90% – even in countries with low rates of HIV infection.
- Trends concerning hepatitis B are difficult to identify because the presence of antibodies may indicate vaccination rather than infection.

- Risk behaviours that may transmit infection are of concern. High-risk groups include: young injectors not exposed to earlier education campaigns; women, who tend to share injecting equipment more than men; heroin injectors who also use cocaine; and imprisoned drug users.

Other morbidity
Possible long-term neural damage linked to heavy use of ecstasy is a growing concern.
- Increasing numbers of studies with both animals and humans suggest that chronic exposure to ecstasy causes functional and morphological changes in the parts of the brain that regulate physiological and psychological functions such as sleep, appetite, mood, aggression and cognition.
- Some studies report mild cognitive impairment in heavy ecstasy users, but the scientific literature is inconsistent regarding other functions. Other unresolved issues include the 'dangerous' dose range, frequency of use and whether deficits are reversible.
- Use of GHB – which in small doses diminishes tension but in marginally larger doses can cause potentially fatal intoxications, particularly when taken with alcohol and other sedatives – is also causing concern.

Trends in responses to drug use

Policy and strategy developments
New drug strategies have been adopted by Spain, France, Portugal and the UK as well as by the European Union itself.
- National drug policies are becoming more balanced in approach, with greater emphasis placed on demand reduction relative to supply reduction.
- The drug problem is increasingly viewed in a broader social context and common aims include drug prevention, reduction of drug-related harm and crime deterrence.
- Accurate scientific evidence, clear objectives, measurable performance targets and evaluation are key to these strategies.

- Depenalisation of drug use offences is becoming more common. The consensus is emerging that drug users should not be imprisoned because of their addiction, and alternatives provided in law are increasingly implemented.

Prevention
Drug prevention in schools, recreational settings and among high-risk groups is a priority in all EU Member States.
- School drug-prevention programmes combine information for pupils with training in life skills such as self-assertiveness. Peer-group approaches actively involve young people in implementing prevention activities in their schools.
- Specific training and guidelines for teachers, as well as initiatives targeting parents, are increasingly being developed.
- Use of the Internet as an educational tool for pupils, teachers and parents alike is growing.
- Drug-prevention training for youth workers, night-club and bar staff is being introduced in some countries.
- Prevention of synthetic drug use is becoming more professional, combining information, outreach work, counselling and sometimes pill testing.
- Local cross-sector youth policies are being developed to meet the needs of high-risk groups.

- Evaluation methodology to assess outreach work with high-risk groups is urgently needed and the EMCDDA is developing guidelines to bridge this gap.

Reducing the harmful consequences of drug use
Reducing the harmful consequences of drug use is key to the drug strategies of many Member States.
- Syringe-exchange programmes are expanding across the EU and activities are intensifying to counter falling awareness of the risks of injecting.
- Outreach work and low-threshold services are growing as a complement to conventional drug-treatment centres.
- 'Users' rooms', where drugs can be consumed under hygienic and supervised conditions, remain controversial and a study funded by the European Commission is evaluating their effectiveness.

Treatment
To cope with the growing numbers and divergent needs of those seeking treatment for drug use, diversified patterns of care are being developed throughout the EU.
- Co-operation has increased between youth and social services and conventional drug services, which alone are often inadequate to treat new drug-use patterns and new target groups.

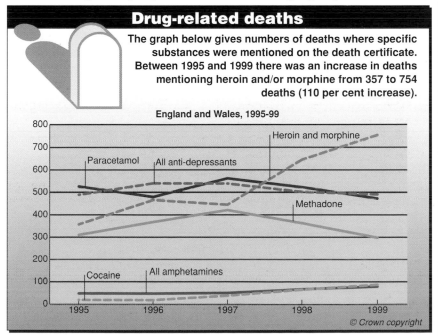

Drug-related deaths

The graph below gives numbers of deaths where specific substances were mentioned on the death certificate. Between 1995 and 1999 there was an increase in deaths mentioning heroin and/or morphine from 357 to 754 deaths (110 per cent increase).

England and Wales, 1995-99

Paracetamol — All anti-depressants — Heroin and morphine — Methadone — Cocaine — All amphetamines

- Specialised services for women exist across the EU, many specifically targeting pregnant women and mothers with children, as well as female sex workers.
- Public-health and psychiatric services are increasingly involved in the treatment of multiple-drug use.
- Substitution treatment is expanding – including in prisons – both in terms of the numbers of clients and the substances used.
- Awareness of the need for adequate after-care for drug users

Cannabis remains the most widely available and commonly used drug across the EU, with substantial increases in use over the 1990s

leaving treatment or prison – or for those in long-term substitution treatment – has risen considerably.

- A large proportion of the prison population are drug users and treatment is increasingly provided to avoid relapse into illegal drug use and crime.

• The above information is from the European Monitoring Centre for Drugs and Drug Addiction (EMCDDA). See page 41 for address details or visit their web site at www.emcdda.org

© *Annual report on the state of the drugs problem in the European Union 2000 (Lisbon: EMCDDA, 2000). pp. 7-10.*

Confident kids likely to try drugs

By Jason Burke

Young people with high self-esteem are more likely to take illicit drugs than those whose self-confidence is low, new research has revealed.

The findings contradict the conventional wisdom that drug-taking is most prevalent among anxious or insecure youth looking for an escape from poor conditions or a way to feel better about themselves.

Instead, up to 27 per cent of young people with high self-esteem had used illicit substances compared with only 20 per cent of their less self-confident peers. Experts say the new research means an overhaul of drug education programmes is necessary.

The survey of 15,000 children aged 14 and 15 was conducted by the respected Schools Health Education Unit (SHEU) in Exeter.

On most occasions the drug tried was cannabis, though solvents and amphetamines also featured in responses, said David Regis, who led the research team.

'Unfortunately the results blow a hole in the simple moral fable that young people are led into the paths of righteousness by high self-esteem,' he said.

Two factors are thought to explain the results. More confident children are more likely to be sociable, have more money and thus have more opportunity to experiment with drugs. And they are also often more willing to indulge in 'risk-taking' activities, ranging from extreme sports to class-A drugs.

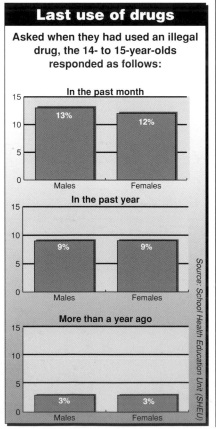

Last use of drugs

Asked when they had used an illegal drug, the 14- to 15-year-olds responded as follows:

In the past month

13% Males   12% Females

In the past year

9% Males   9% Females

More than a year ago

3% Males   3% Females

Source: School Health Education Unit (SHEU)

Research reveals that though youngsters who describe themselves as 'experimental' cigarette smokers often have low self-esteem, those who call themselves 'committed' smokers have self-esteem levels as high or higher than average.

Heather Ashton, a professor of pharmacology at Newcastle University who has studied patterns of drug-taking among students, said last week that the results of the SHEU survey did not surprise her: 'Students all report they take drugs for pleasure and that it has nothing to do with anxiety or stress. Years ago young people who did [drugs] were seen as psychotic or low or risk-takers. Now that is not the case.'

Ashton's research shows that one in five university students says he or she uses cannabis at least once a week. It also shows that a typical cannabis joint in the Sixties contained only 10mg of a potent chemical known as THC which affects the brain. The typical joint now, with more sophisticated cultivation and plant breeding, contains more than 150mg and has a far more potent effect.

The report detailed the damage long-term use of cannabis can do to cognitive ability, memory, co-ordination and the cardiovascular and respiratory systems.

© *Guardian Newspapers Limited 2001*

The psychological effects of street drugs

Information from MIND. Written by Terry Brown and edited by Sara Dunn

There is a lot of concern about the increasing use of illegal or 'street' drugs, and their possible effects on physical and mental health. However, media information can often be inaccurate and sensationalised.

Research on illegal drugs tends to concentrate on chemical composition, and effects on laboratory animals. Few long-term studies on illegal drug users have been carried out. Because of society's attitudes to illegal drug users, truly objective studies are quite scarce.

At the same time the use of illegal drugs is now an unsensational part of youth culture, some research indicating that up to half of young people have experimented with illegal drugs or solvents by the time they leave school at 16.

The information given here concerns the general effects of street drugs on the mental health of all those who might use them. Specific issues concerning the use of street drugs by people with existing mental health problems – sometimes referred to as people who have a 'dual diagnosis' – will be addressed in separate Mind publications.

Why do people start to use illegal drugs?

The main reason people start to use drugs and continue to use them is that they find the experience enjoyable. A number of factors may encourage people to start, including availability, curiosity, rebellion, peer influence and peer preference. But in most cases they are offered the opportunity by a friend they trust, who wants them to enjoy the same kind of experience they have had.

What are the patterns of drug use?

There are four discernible, but overlapping patterns of drug use. It is useful to bear in mind legal drug use (for example caffeine, alcohol,

---

Some people try some drugs a number of times before they decide whether they want to carry on using them or not

---

tobacco, medicines, and any others) when you read these explanations, as they are as applicable to legal drugs as they are to street drugs.

Abstinence

This means that a person is not taking a particular drug at the time. They may have never tried it, or they may have experimented with it and not liked it, or have used it regularly and stopped.

Experimentation

This means trying something out; it is usually a conscious decision, taking into account the influences pertaining at the time. Some people try some drugs a number of times before they decide whether they want to carry on using them or not. Some drugs (for example cannabis) may have little effect the first time, which may make the person consider whether it is worth taking. Others may be unpleasant the first time (for example smoking cigarettes), and persistence may be required before the 'benefits' are realised. The majority of people who experiment with illegal drugs and solvents do not continue using them.

- YOU PREFER DRUGS TO REALITY?!

- REALITY SHOULD LIFT ITS GAME...

Casual/recreational/regular use

If a person decides to carry on using a particular drug, they may use it casually, recreationally or regularly. A casual drug user will use a particular drug when it is easily available, and not be too concerned when it is not, as well as not feeling they need it to enhance their enjoyment of situations.

A recreational user will use their drugs of choice for specific effects on specific occasions. Alcohol, caffeine and tobacco are used in a variety of circumstances for recreational reasons, as are, for example, cannabis, LSD and ecstasy. A regular user will take their drug(s) of choice most days, or (with some drugs), most weeks.

With most drugs, each of these patterns of use may have undesirable effects on the individual. However, the great majority of drug users feel that their existence is enhanced by their drug use, and that they suffer no adverse consequences; they do not fall into the fourth pattern – problem drug use.

Dependent/problem/chaotic use

Recreational or regular use may slip into dependent, problem or chaotic use for a variety of reasons, which may be to do with the person, their situation, or the drug(s) they are using. A physical dependence may develop to some particular drugs, because after long-term regular use the body may require the drug in order to function normally. A psychological dependence may also develop with some drugs, making the person think they cannot function without them.

Problem drug use may involve adverse physical, social, legal, financial or mental health consequences. Chaotic drug use implies that obtaining and taking the drug(s) are the central and most important aspects of a person's life, and everything else is of little consequence.

This chaotic pattern is the least common by far, and may be reached a long time after experimentation – though for a very small number of individuals it can follow fairly quickly. People who are in this pattern of drug use are not *necessarily*

Problem drug use may bring to the surface, reinforce or exacerbate existing or latent mental health problems

---

stuck there, and may, with the appropriate motivation and support, return to the other patterns.

Problem drug use may bring to the surface, reinforce or exacerbate existing or latent mental health problems. But cause and effect are difficult to separate in this situation, with the interaction of different factors on the drug user complicating any assessment. Problem drug use may include an element of self-medication; for example, taking amphetamines to increase confidence, anabolic steroids to change body image, or heroin to withdraw from an unpleasant reality.

What are the effects of drug use?

The effects of using a drug vary greatly. They are influenced by the type of drug, the amount taken, previous experience of the drug, what the user wants and expects to happen, the environment and social situation in which it is taken, and the mental state of the user.

The same person may react differently to the same drug at

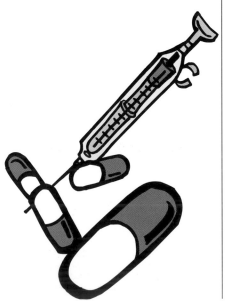

different times. A tolerance may build up with some drugs, in which the body gets used to the repeated presence of a drug, so that higher doses are needed to maintain the same effect. Withdrawal is the body's reaction to the sudden absence of a drug to which it has adapted; the effects can be stopped either by taking more of the drug, or by 'cold turkey', which may last up to a week.

There are four main groups of drugs, divided according to the major effect they have (or for which people take them).

Stimulants

These include caffeine and tobacco as well as amphetamines, anabolic steroids, 'poppers', hallucinogenic amphetamines (ecstasy), cocaine and crack. They act on the central nervous system to increase neural activity in the brain. With the exception of steroids and 'poppers', stimulants increase alertness, diminish fatigue, delay sleep, increase ability to maintain vigilance or perform physical tasks over a long period, and elevate mood. With all except tobacco, high doses can cause nervousness and anxiety. With the exception of tobacco and caffeine, stimulants can cause temporary paranoid psychosis. Withdrawal effects include hunger and fatigue, but these seldom require medical assistance.

Depressants

These include alcohol, benzo-diazepines (minor tranquillisers such as Valium, Librium, Mogadon and temazepam), solvents, glues, aerosols and gases. Depressants act on the central nervous system to suppress neural activity in the brain. They relieve tension and anxiety, promote relaxation, impair the efficiency of mental and physical functioning, and decrease self-control.

Analgesics

Analgesics are painkillers, and include heroin, opium, pethidine and codeine. They reduce sensitivity to emotional reaction and physical pain. They produce feelings of warmth and contentment, with relatively little interference in mental or physical functioning.

Hallucinogens

These include cannabis, LSD and 'magic' mushrooms. The hallucinogens heighten appreciation of sensory experiences, and may induce perceptual distortions, feelings of dissociation or insight, elevation of mood, and hallucinations.

What about mixing drugs?

Mixing of drugs, purposely or inadvertently, can be at best unpredictable, and at worst, fatal. This is particularly true of mixing any two in the depressant or analgesic categories, which may lead to unconsciousness, coma or death because of the combined effects. This does not apply just to illegal drugs many people may be unaware of the adverse consequences of using street drugs while taking prescribed medicines.

Useful addresses

Scottish Association for Mental Health. Tel: 0141 568 7000.

Northern Ireland Association for Mental Health. Tel: 02890 328474.

Mind (National Association for Mental Health), Granta House, 15-19 Broadway, London, E15 4BQ.

• For details of your nearest Mind association and of local services contact Mind's helpline, Mind*info*Line: 020 8522 1728 (within London) or 0845 7660 163 (outside London) Mon-Fri 9.15am – 4.45pm. For interpretation, Mind*info*Line has access to 100 languages via Language Line. Typetalk is available for people with hearing or speech problems who have access to a minicom. To make a call via Typetalk dial 0800 959598, fax: 0151 709 8119.

The above information is an extract from *Understanding the psychological effects of street drugs*, a title from the 'Understanding' series produced by Mind. Other publications in the 'Understanding' series include: Anxiety, Bereavement, Dementia, Depression, Eating Distress, Learning Disability, Manic Depression, Mental Illness, Phobias and Obsessions and Self-Harm.

Most of these are recorded on standard cassette, and can be borrowed by visually impaired people from RNIB Customer Service, PO Box 173, Peterborough PE2 6WS, Tel. 0345 023153. For a full publications list send a stamped addressed envelope to Mind Mail Order, 15-19 Broadway, London E15 4BQ.

• Mind works for a better life for everyone with experience of mental distress.

© *Mind*

More than 80% of street beggars are taking drugs

By Nicole Martin

Most homeless people who beg on the streets take drugs, according to research published yesterday.

The Government issued its Rough Sleepers' Unit findings as it faced criticism of its £240,000 advertising campaign urging the public not to give money to beggars. According to the research, more than eight in 10 take some form of illegal drugs, of whom nearly half use heroin, 35 per cent take crack, and 18 per cent take cocaine.

More than half of the 260 people canvassed said they drank alcohol, and of those 54 per cent did so every day and spent more than £30 a week on drink. More than one in 10 said they earned more than £50 a day through begging.

Shelter, the homeless charity, dismissed the Change A Life scheme launched yesterday as 'misjudged' and said the campaign risked worsening the stigma attached to some of the most vulnerable people in society. Chris Holmes, the charity's director, said: 'If people are forced to find other ways to maintain a drugs habit, they may be forced into more serious crime, or working for drug dealers.'

Newspaper, magazine and radio advertisements will soon urge the public to give their money to charity, do voluntary work for homeless

> '**Research has shown that people who are begging on the streets are begging for one very sad reason – because they are addicted to drugs'**

organisations or provide beggars with blankets and other gifts rather than cash.

Louise Casey, head of the Government's Rough Sleepers' Unit, said the initiative was based on evidence that rough sleepers used a large proportion of their income to finance their drug and alcohol addictions. She said: 'Few people can walk past a human being lying on a doorway with their hands held out and not be moved. But research has shown that people who are begging on the streets are begging for one very sad reason – because they are addicted to drugs.'

Mo Mowlam, the Cabinet Office Minister, denied that the Government's campaign was 'anti-begging'. She said: 'If you want to give money, give it. But if you want to give in a way that will change a life of somebody on the streets, then think again.'

© *Telegraph Group Limited, London 2000*

Drug misuse

Information from the Florence Nightingale Hospitals

The most commonly used legal drug in our society is caffeine, which is found in tea, coffee, chocolate and some minerals. The next most commonly used drug is alcohol. Tobacco is the third most popular drug.

There has, however, been a relentless increase in the use of illegal drugs in recent decades, particularly among young people. Approximately 2000 people die a year from drug misuse.

Drug classification

There are 3 classes of controlled drugs classified in the Misuse of Drugs Act (1971) as those being forbidden or limited to medical channels, each has its own guideline for penalty:

Class A – heroin, crack, LSD (acid), MDMA, cocaine, ecstasy, magic mushrooms, amphetamine (if prepared for injection)

Class B – cannabis, amphetamine (speed)

Class C – supply of anabolic steroids and benzodiazepines, rohypnol

Some other drugs are controlled by the Medicines Act. While it isn't illegal to possess drugs such as GHB or Ketamine, supply is still an offence. The law handles alcohol, gases, glues and aerosols, poppers and tobacco differently.

Drug misuse

DrugScope has collated a wide range of research studies document-ing drug misuse in the UK. Their statistics show that cannabis is the most widely used illegal drug, accounting for up to 80% of illegal drug use. One in seven of the population has used cannabis. Among school-age children, 38% of 15- 16-year-olds in 1995 had taken up the drug – that increased from 30% in 1994, so this figure will have increased further to date. Similar rates of consumption are found for the 16-19 age group.

The most significant rise in drug

use over the last decade has been the rise of 'dance/rave' drugs – most commonly amphetamines, LSD and ecstasy. The use of these drugs is greatest among the 16-24-year-age group.

The use of cocaine (charlie, coke, rock, snow, golddust, lady, wash), crack cocaine (crack, rock, wash, stone) and heroin (smack, H, skag, junk) is also increasing.

Benzodiazepines are the most commonly prescribed minor tran-quillisers for daytime anxiety relief and hypnotics to promote sleep. These include valium, temazepam and mogadon. These drugs can also be misused.

Addiction implies that a drug dependency has developed to such an extent that it has serious detri-mental effects on the user. The term addiction is inextricably linked to society's reaction to the user and so medical experts prefer to use dependence instead.

A drug dependency causes physical, social and/or psychological problems.

Dependence syndrome is a cluster of physiological, behavioural and cognitive phenomena in which the use of a substance takes on a

higher priority for a given individual than other behaviours that once had greater value. A descriptive characteristic is the desire to take a substance. Return to drug use after a period of abstinence can lead to a more rapid reappearance of other features of the syndrome than would occur with non-dependent individuals.

Side-effects of drug taking

There are physical risks attached to drug taking. These risks arise from the nature of the drug, how much is taken, what the drug is cut with (what the pure form is diluted with), means of delivery and more.

The toxic effects of specific drugs cause short- and long-term effects and damage:

Physical

- Dilated eye pupils
- Bloodshot eyes
- Blurred vision
- Dry mouth and throat, de-hydration
- Nausea
- Stomach cramps
- Muscle tension
- Chills
- Sweating

- Blackouts
- Flashbacks
- Increased blood pressure
- Weight loss
- Increased heart rate
- Cardiac arrhythmia/heart problems, heart disease, heart attack
- Seizures
- Respiratory/lung failure
- Lung cancer

Psychological

- Acute psychotic reactions
- Anxiety
- Paranoia
- Personality change

Behavioural

- Mental impairment
- Confusion
- Increased risk of accidents
- Apathy
- Sleeplessness
- Disorientated behaviour, nervous erratic behaviour
- Staring into space
- Hallucinations

Warning signs of drug use

- Constant sniffing
- Sudden irregular mood swings/irritability/anger/hostility
- Sullen uncaring attitude and behaviour
- Gradual loss of interest in hobbies/sport/activities
- Loss of motivation, energy, self-discipline
- Staying out more, possibly in new places/with new people
- Reduced interest in personal grooming/dress and hygiene
- Unhealthy appearance
- Excessive tiredness, change in sleeping patterns
- Use of cologne/deodorants/room air fresheners to hide smells
- Pipes, small boxes or containers, rolling papers or other unusual items
- Sores and rashes, especially around mouth and nose
- Excessive spending or borrowing of money
- Decline in work/school performance
- Absenteeism, declining work
- Forgetfulness – short or long term
- Loss of appetite
- Trouble with the law

Withdrawal is the body's reaction to the sudden absence of a drug to which it has adapted – this is called 'cold turkey', this physical reaction can last for up to a week. These withdrawal symptoms can range from psychological and physical disruptions ranging from mild anxiety and tremor/shaking to acute psychosis and other more dangerous problems. The effects can be stopped by taking more of the drug.

Drug use patterns

Internal distress, limited life opportunities and unhappiness can predispose an individual to using drugs. The following stages also explain the reasons for the use of drugs further:

Experimental use/contact stage
- Person tries out drugs to satisfy curiosity about their effects, boredom, peer pressure, protest, feel good.
- For many people, drug use stops or remains at this level.

Recreational use stage
- Person uses drugs in a regular pattern over a period of time.

Regular use stage
- Person uses drugs to alter mood in friendly settings and at parties or to be sociable.
- Use can be situational (to celebrate or for stress or depression) or spree/binge type.

Excessive use stage
- User spends a great deal of time, energy and money on getting and using one or more drugs.
- Drug use may be solitary or take place in social situations where drug use is the central activity or main reason for the get-together.
- Preoccupation with the quality and effects of drugs becomes noticeable.
- Psychological and physical impairment become apparent.
- Daily functioning is noticeably affected.
- Responsibilities are neglected.
- Relationships with others may become strained and go downhill rapidly.

- Family members (enablers) may find themselves making excuses for the drug user or taking over his or her responsibilities.
- Many heavy drinkers who do not consider themselves alcoholics are in this stage.

Dependent use stage
- Person uses drugs to hold off withdrawal symptoms, which occur after development of physical and psychological dependence. Cold turkey is the name given if rapid withdrawal from drugs takes place.
- Individual's entire perspective for dealing with reality is drug controlled.

Problem drug use tends to refer to drug use which could either be dependent or recreational. It is the effects that drug-taking has on the user's life

Treatment

Admitting or recognising an addiction problem is the largest and hardest step forward and until this is achieved, the recovery process cannot begin.

Treatment for drug misuse is available in many forms depending on individual needs (including severity) and circumstances (including family and social support).

A comprehensive treatment programme would be discussed from an initial assessment with a specialist – this could be a drug and alcohol counsellor or a Consultant Psychiatrist.

Treatment may be as an in-patient, residential, day-patient or out-patient, depending on individual needs. Duration of treatment will depend on the severity of the problem and on the person's circumstances. Normally it can last for up to 4 weeks, but the person will also be seen at regular intervals during the year after treatment.

Treatment of drug dependency involves treating both the physical and psychological problems that result from drug use. Medical treatment may be necessary for health problems (e.g. liver damage), if the person is physically dependent (e.g. detoxification) or if maintenance therapy is necessary.

Where abstinence is indicated, treatment is structured and involves stages, the aim being to help the person to abstain from drugs completely.

Detoxification is the first step in treatment for people who are physically dependent on drugs (withdrawal symptoms will occur when drug use stops).

Detoxification can be provided within a hospital setting, as an out-patient or in the home. The place of treatment would need to be discussed on assessment.

Detoxification is safe, is supervised by trained medical specialists and usually takes about 10-14 days. It involves replacing the substance with other drugs and reducing the dose of these over the treatment period. This minimises the unpleasant symptoms that result when stopping drug use.

People who are unwilling to manage complete abstinence can still be offered treatment.

Maintenance therapy prescribes a substitute drug for which 'cross tolerance' exists. The goal is to reduce the use of a particular drug or to reduce the harm caused by a particular method of administration. The most well-known form of maintenance therapy is the prescribing of methadone to wean people off opioids.

Rehabilitative treatment therapy is the next stage of treatment and involves group and individual therapy. The aim is to help the person address the reasons behind their drug use, looking at their attitudes to drugs and issues surrounding personal relationships.

A treatment programme known as 'the Twelve-step programme' is often implemented at this stage. The programme was devised by Alcoholics Anonymous and involves the user admitting powerlessness over their life and drug use, making up for past 'wrongs' and offering help to other sufferers. Programmes encourage self-knowledge, self-esteem, relapse prevention, building support systems and awareness of problems as a result of the drug problem.

Relapse prevention is a form of therapeutic rehabilitation that aims to help people avoid returning to uncontrolled drug use. People most commonly relapse when they experience a negative emotion such as frustration, anger, anxiety or depression. Relapse may also be triggered by interpersonal conflict and peer pressure. Cravings account for less than 10% of relapses. In relapse prevention, people are shown coping mechanisms to be implemented if necessary.

The objective is to develop a positive approach to daily living and develop alternatives to drinking. This stage, which lasts for approximately 4 weeks, can be emotionally exhausting and may result in undesirable behaviour such as mood swings.

Therapeutic communities have their place in rehabilitation. They are in geographically isolated areas and are highly structured to help people with drug-related problems try to work through these prior to

returning to the community. This stage of treatment can last for a number of months, depending on individual needs and progress.

Self-help groups may also be involved at this stage, e.g. narcotics anonymous. Research also points to the powerful role played by the self-help groups and shows that attendance on a regular basis can help people to grow emotionally and spiritually.

If you are a relative or friend

Acceptance and treatment for drug dependency can be a stressful time for anyone, because of underlying problems that need to be confronted and resolved. Support and understanding from family and friends is a vital part of successful treatment.

Any problem that a loved one is experiencing can be hard to understand, and cope with and distressing for those who are close. Family therapy aims to help and support your difficulties too and is available.

How to get help
Addiction programme

This material is for information purposes only and a GP or a qualified professional should be consulted to provide further advice to meet your individual needs. This is not intended to replace qualified medical advice and should not be used to assume a diagnosis. Please consult your GP or a qualified professional to identify a diagnosis and/or commence any type of treatment.

© Florence Nightingale Hospitals

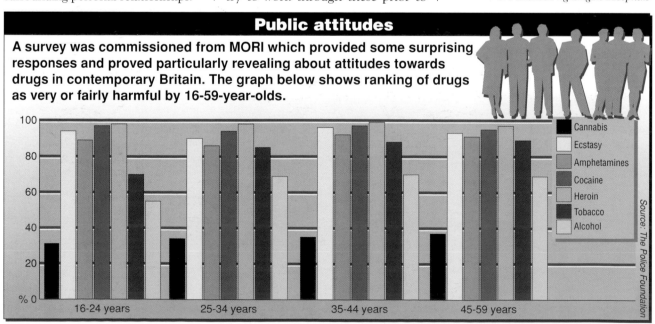

Public attitudes

A survey was commissioned from MORI which provided some surprising responses and proved particularly revealing about attitudes towards drugs in contemporary Britain. The graph below shows ranking of drugs as very or fairly harmful by 16-59-year-olds.

Cannabis
Ecstasy
Amphetamines
Cocaine
Heroin
Tobacco
Alcohol

Source: The Police Foundation

Myths about young people and drugs

Information from Lifeline

Nobody knows exactly how many young people use drugs. Surveys of school children in Britain tend to show between a quarter and a half have used drugs by their 16th birthday depending upon the area they live in. What is generally true is that by the age of 16 using an illegal drug is no longer confined to a deviant minority. If your child does not grow up using drugs, they will almost certainly know somebody who does. On top of this nearly all children will drink alcohol and many will end up smoking cigarettes.

What are parents to make of all this? If we believe the TV and newspapers all of our children are being turned into junkies and will end up dead. Many young people see it very differently and talk about enjoying using drugs and say parents exaggerate the dangers involved.

What is the truth about young people's drug use? There is a lot of misinformation and there are so many myths. This information will help you learn the facts and avoid the myths. You don't have to be a walking encyclopaedia on drugs but you do need accurate information. Read the pamphlet but remember the best place to start is to *talk and listen* to your youngsters about drugs. A bit of honesty and give or take will help you both.

The main drugs used:
Cannabis – is by far the most widely used illegal drug
LSD, *poppers*, *ecstasy*, *amphetamines*, *solvents*, *magic mushrooms and cocaine* – are all used by a sizeable minority
Heroin and rock cocaine are still thankfully only used by a small minority of people

'It is a new thing'
Drug use is not a new thing. There has been drug use throughout history and there are plenty of examples of drug scares and panics in the past. However, the trend is changing.

'They're all at it'
As we said before, more young people are using drugs. New drugs have come

> ### What is the truth about young people's drug use? There is a lot of misinformation and there are so many myths

on the scene and drug taking is starting at an earlier age. There are plenty of young people in every secondary school who have used drugs. It is no good pretending that it is not happening but it is also important to keep it in perspective. Not every youngster tries illegal drugs and many who do only use them occasionally.

'They're all going to die'
Thankfully most who try drugs will not come to any serious harm. Many will either just have an occasional dabble or use more often but carefully, much as many adults limit their drinking. Not everyone who drinks alcohol dies of alcohol poisoning.

'It only happens in deprived inner-city areas'
One clear trend is that drug use is not just in inner-city, deprived areas but also common in the leafy, middle-class suburbs. Young people and drugs travel easily.

'Boys use more than girls'
Using drugs used to be much more common among boys than girls but this has also changed. Recent surveys of young people show girls are fast

catching up on boys. This might have something to do with the way girls mature quicker than boys and often mix with boys who are older than themselves. It also might have something to do with the fact that young girls can more easily get into pubs and clubs where drugs may be available and used.

'There is something wrong with young people who use drugs'

Today using drugs is a very normal thing for many young people. It does not mean there is necessarily anything wrong with these young people. They may well see drug use as fun and something that makes them feel good, lowers their inhibitions and is part of a good night out. Young people love testing out new things and it can seem even more attractive if adults tell them not to do it. It is not easy to say exactly why they use. It could be for all sorts of reasons and will vary from person to person.

'They do it for the same reasons'

Why a young person dabbles or experiments a few times will be very different from why they might use regularly. Some young people use regularly but in a very controlled, what we call recreational way. The reasons why this small minority use so heavily will have something to do with emotional or social problems they face. They will use drugs to try to escape what they see as a harsh world rather than to just have a good time with friends. People use drugs in different ways and for different reasons.

'They do it because they are bored'

It is not as simple as saying they do it because they are bored. Lots of young people who have active lives also use drugs.

'They do it because of peer pressure'

They also may be encouraged to do it because of friends or to try to fit in with the crowd but there is also a lot of pressure not to use drugs.

Occasionally some young people may be forced or tricked into using drugs but it usually has more to do with choice than pressure. Anyway, what do we mean by peer pressure? We rarely use the term to apply to adults or ourselves.

'They do it because they mix with the wrong sort'

We often think youngsters use drugs because they get in with 'the wrong sort' but who are 'the wrong sort'? Too often we like to blame drug use on someone else rather than realising that, whether we like it or not, a lot of young people freely choose to use drugs. When you look at the growth in young people's drug use it could include our own children however we have brought them up.

• The above information is an extract from *Drug Myths! – a parent's guide*, produced by Lifeline Publications. See page 41 for address details.

Drugs homework at primary school

Parents will be requested to do 'drugs homework' with children as young as five under Government plans to reduce drug abuse.

The proposals, which are being prepared by Keith Hellawell, the Government's anti-drugs co-ordinator, are intended to ensure that pupils, and their parents, are fully aware of the dangers of different substances.

The plans have been prompted by concern that many parents, particularly those in middle-class or rural areas, are failing to protect their children because they are 'in denial' about the risk of them taking drugs. Critics warned that the homework could backfire by raising awareness of drugs and increasing the likelihood of experimentation.

Mr Hellawell insisted, however, that all parents needed to teach their children about drugs to create a

By Martin Bentham, Social Affairs Correspondent

'family aversion' to abuse. He said: 'We are looking at as many ways as possible to get parents involved. One of the ways is if we do homework on drugs. Drugs homework will bind in parents. We want to engage parents in understanding these issues.'

Homework would begin at five with lessons about 'pills and capsules' used at home, progressing to alcohol, tobacco, solvents and hard drugs as pupils became older

'Young achievers from stable backgrounds are very vulnerable and are a fast-growing group of drug experimenters. The first thing we want to do is to get parents to recognise that it could happen to their child.'

Mr Hellawell said that homework would begin at five with lessons about 'pills and capsules' used at home, progressing to alcohol, tobacco, solvents and hard drugs as pupils became older.

John Dunford, of the Secondary Heads' Association, said it might be useful for older pupils but should not be a regular feature. He said: 'The appropriate place for drugs education is in school because teachers can conduct it there in an informed and controlled manner. Setting homework on drugs would not be helpful.'

Drug safety – the basics

Information from Gary Hayes, DrugScope

What follows are some starters giving you practical guidelines relating to drugs whether they are legal or not. All of the facts are current. However remember that laws and practices are constantly changing, so always check if unsure.

- As we all know, the way to avoid risks with drugs is to leave them alone. But if you are going to take them, know as much as possible about drugs and the risks that come with taking them.
- If you are going to use drugs, make sure you are with friends. It's not a good idea to be on your own – being with friends can help when you come down.
- Always tell each other what you're taking, so if one of you runs into trouble of any sort, the others will know what to do. (See 'First Aid'.)
- The effects of drugs can vary according to where you are, who you're with, how you're feeling emotionally at the time and how physically fit you are.
- Also, the less you weigh, the more powerful the effect.
- It's best to avoid drugs if you're feeling depressed or anxious – they could make you feel worse.
- Be especially careful if you're taking prescribed drugs – there may be reactions you're not prepared for.
- Don't drive. Alcohol and drugs affect your perceptions and reaction times. The police are looking out more for drivers using drugs and you could lose your licence.
- Try not to buy from strangers, you can never be sure of what you're buying. Drugs are not quality controlled so you never know what's in them. They may be stronger/purer than you anticipate, or you may just get ripped off.
- Drugs can often be very expensive – so try not to borrow off friends or buy on credit from dealers and set a limit on what you are going to spend.
- Many drugs make you feel more confident or stimulated sexually, but always try to practise safer sex for obvious health reasons – risk of sexually transmitted diseases, HIV infection, unwanted pregnancy.
- If you are pregnant, you may experience effects from drugs you don't anticipate. It could also affect your baby. If you are breast feeding, any drugs you are taking can be passed to the baby in breast milk.
- If you are injecting drugs, never inject alone. Always use clean needles and equipment and don't share equipment.
- Remember that if you are caught with an illegal drug by the police, you may be prosecuted and this will result in you having a criminal record – something many employers are very wary of.

Going out

If you go clubbing or out to an all-night party there are a number of things to look out for. All premises such as clubs, discos or college events are bound by the Entertainment Licensing Laws and must provide a number of facilities.

Make the management aware if:
- it's too hot or too crowded.
- drinking water taps don't work or there's no free cold water available.
- you have difficulty with security or door staff – write down their name and registration number.
- one of your friends is ill and you're not properly assisted (See 'First Aid').

Tell your local council's Environmental Health Dept, or the college authorities if no action is seen to be taken. (Details taken from the London Drug Policy Forum's code of good practice for clubs, *Dance till Dawn – Safely*. For a copy, or further information, see the 'Contact' list. If your club/ college hasn't seen one, it can be sent a copy.)

First aid

What to do if someone is ill:

Getting emergency help
If trouble strikes, the following recommendations apply for any location.

On campus

All universities and colleges have a first aid room and many staff there are trained in recovery.

Emergency numbers will be posted in all halls of residence and caretaker staff can find help. If in doubt, always ask for an ambulance to be called – do it yourself if necessary. Give the medical staff all the help they need to identify what happened and what drugs were involved.

In a club

Good clubs have at least one first aider or paramedic who knows about drugs. Ask a staff member for the first aider and if you have trouble, demand to see the manager. There may be drugs outreach workers who can help – club staff will know if they are in the club, and where.

First aid

If you know, tell the first aider or paramedic what drugs have been taken. They are not interested in legalities, but want to help your friend, so the drug information is vital. If you do not know try collecting a sample of vomit if there is any. This can be tested to see what they have taken. It sounds disgusting but it may save a life. Alternatively you can give a sample of the drug if any is left.

If someone collapses

Put the person in the recovery position, then send for help.

Recovery position

If the person is breathing, turn them on to their front, with their head sideways. Bend their upper arm and leg. Straighten the other arm parallel to their back. Either stay with them, asking stewards to clear a space or, if possible, move them, still in the recovery position, to a quieter place.

If they are not breathing, and you know how to do mouth-to-mouth resuscitation, do so. If not, wait until someone arrives who does. In the meantime, loosen tight clothing.

Recognising heat exhaustion, heat stroke and overheating

It is not just being hot. Symptoms could include any or many of the following: dizziness, feeling sick, sudden tiredness, sudden headache or cramps, particularly in the arms and legs. Peeing is difficult and it's dark in colour. Sweating stops, which is a strong signal of dangerously increasing body heat. Blackouts, collapsing, fits or fainting can follow.

Anyone suffering from any of these symptoms should immediately take a break, cool down in the quieter area or chill out room and sip about a pint of water slowly. Gulping down a great deal of water should be avoided. Cool or tepid water splashed on the head and neck helps with cooling down, so will wrapping them in cool damp towels. (As a general rule, when dancing, sip about a pint of water per hour slowly.)

If the body gets back to normal temperature, try to find dry or warmer clothes or a blanket – don't over-chill.

Anxiety

If someone is getting anxious or is hallucinating, take them away from bright lights, loud music and crowds to somewhere quiet and warm, possibly familiar. Talk to them, calm them down, give them support. If they do not respond, stay with them and send a friend for help.

Recognising serious problems

If you see any of the following symptoms, get medical help – send for an ambulance immediately.

Alcohol – can become unconscious and vomit in sleep. Delirium may reveal alcohol poisoning.

Cocaine – overdose leads to confusion and dizziness, combined with a dry throat. Erratic breathing, short gasps followed by deep gulps.

Speed – can cause collapse.

Ecstasy – hyperventilation, over-heating and unconsciousness.

Solvents – convulsions, becoming unconscious.

Poppers – poisonous if swallowed. Can cause fainting and collapse.

Magic mushrooms – eating the wrong type of mushroom can cause diarrhoea, vomiting, cramps, breathing difficulties, loss of consciousness and, in some cases, death.

GHB – overdose symptoms are convulsions, coma and inability to breath. Mixed with alcohol can cause collapse and convulsions.

Ketamine – temporary paralysis, nausea, vomiting and slurring of speech.

Heroin – overdose causes slow, or erratic breathing, pinpoint pupils, semi-consciousness with little or no response. Lips and skin turn blue. Blood pressure falls. Coma and death can follow.

Useful contacts

Drinkline
Tel: 0845 601 4357

Advice and support for parents
ADFAM
Tel: 020 7928 8900

Information on other local services plus free advice and help:
National Drugs Helpline
Tel: 0800 776600

Information, policy guidance and research about drugs:
Drugscope
Tel: 020 7928 1211

Legal and welfare advice and outreach work at dance events
Release
from 10 am to 6 pm Tel: 020 7729 9904/5255 or at other times Tel: 020 7603 8654

Help with drugs and clubs
London Drug Policy Forum
(for 'Dance till Dawn – Safely') Tel: 020 7332 3484/3084

© DrugScope

Seven in 10 offenders test positive for drugs

By Nick Hopkins,
Crime Correspondent

Some crack cocaine and heroin users are committing up to 240 burglaries a year to fund their habits, generating an illegal annual income of £13,000 each, the Home Office revealed yesterday.

Research also suggests that more offenders are suffering from serious drug problems than there were three years ago. Fieldwork in Liverpool, Nottingham, Sunderland and South Norwood, in south London, showed 69% of people arrested tested positive for drugs.

According to the New-Adam (new English and Welsh arrestee drug abuse monitoring) study, the number of people arrested who tested positive for heroin in Nottingham doubled between 1997 and 1999. The proportion of offenders using crack cocaine rose from 10% to 23%.

Across the four areas, heroin and crack cocaine users were four times more likely to shoplift and five times more likely to commit robbery than offenders using other drugs.

The Home Office insisted the figures had to be treated with caution because the work, commissioned as part of an ongoing review of the government's anti-drugs strategy, was based on small samples and was already dated.

However, Paul Wiles, director of research, development and statistics at the Home Office, said the evidence suggested the situation was deteriorating.

Ministers hope the tide will be turned by two major initiatives. Within two years every police force in England and Wales will have the option of referring arrested offenders to drug treatment programmes. And from October 1, courts will be able to issue drug treatment and testing orders.

Mr Wiles said there was already reason for optimism, pointing to the results of another Home Office funded study published yesterday.

Research into the effectiveness of drug treatment clinics showed they have a huge impact on drug use and drug-related crime. At one unit in Hackney, east London, heroin and cocaine use by addicts fell by 56% over six months.

> **Heroin and crack cocaine users were four times more likely to shoplift and five times more likely to commit robbery than offenders using other drugs**

The treatment, which costs £960, also led to a drop in the illegal earnings of class-A drug users — almost £8,000 in some cases.

Health minister Gisela Stuart said the findings supported the government's proactive approach to drug crime.

She said: 'The results of this research are further resounding proof of the success of treatment in reducing the harm that drugs do to individuals and communities.

'We should be putting significant resources into treatment and prevention rather than responding only to the consequences of drug misuse.'

The government believes its anti-drugs strategy will have made an impact by 2003, and that its programme should not be judged while it is still in the implementation stage.

The National Association for the Care and Resettlement of Offenders said the figures published yesterday strengthened the case for sentencing drug-addicted offenders to treatment rather than imprisonment. Paul Cavadino, Nacro's director of policy, said: 'This could potentially reduce a colossal amount of crime.'

The deputy UK anti-drugs co-ordinator, Mike Trace, said: 'We know from other research that getting such people into treatment can deliver substantial reductions in recorded crime and major improvements to communities as well as having health and social benefits to the individuals and their families. This is why increasing the number of people in treatment is a key aim of the government's strategy.'

21

Drug trafficking

The threat from serious and organised crime

Drug trafficking remains a central feature of organised crime activity. Whilst there is an absence of reliable data on the scale of the market there are indicators of the size of the problem – market profiles, seizure statistics and operational intelligence. Seizures reflect patterns of law enforcement activity as much as the market. Nevertheless this data does provide a rudimentary indicator of supply levels. The level of demand is indicated by the British Crime Survey. The 1998 survey suggests that:

- amphetamine and ecstasy are second in prevalence only to cannabis in the UK. Twenty per cent of 16- to 29-year-olds reported use of amphetamine or something they believed to be amphetamine;
- 10% of 16- to 29-year-olds have tried a drug they believed to be ecstasy;
- 6% of respondents in the 16- to 29-year-age group have tried cocaine – this has doubled since the 1996 survey;
- only 1% reported having tried heroin, although the level of addiction associated with narcotics is an important factor sustaining demand alongside the number of users.

Information from 1999 concerning identified organised crime groups indicates that over half are involved in drug trafficking, though it should be borne in mind that this proportion may reflect the priority given to countering drug trafficking by law enforcement. Over 60% of the identified drug trafficking groups deal in cannabis, over 50% deal in cocaine, between 40 and 50% deal in opiates – including heroin – and over 40% in synthetics. Over 60% of identified drug trafficking groups were involved with more than one type of illegal drug.

Cocaine

Peru, Bolivia and Colombia are the

main sites of coca and cocaine production in the world. Colombia receives most of the coca leaf and paste produced in Peru, while Bolivia is the principal producer of cocaine hydrochloride in the region. Venezuela, Brazil, Ecuador and Panama are main transit countries for cocaine destined for the USA and Europe. It is assessed that because the UK wholesale cocaine price per kg is 10 to 20% higher than elsewhere in Europe, large criminal organisations are currently actively targeting the UK cocaine market.

Importation

Intelligence indicates that Colombian cocaine trafficking groups view Europe as a single market and hence concentrate on shipping large multi-tonne quantities of cocaine to destinations within the European market. These are then broken down and distributed to customers throughout Europe, including the UK.

Recent intelligence points to the Galician province of Spain as being the favoured European entry point for large quantities of cocaine for a number of reasons, including the numerous isolated beaches. Since October 1998, a number of vessels have been intercepted en route to Europe (Spain or the Netherlands) carrying multi-tonne consignments of high-purity cocaine. The port of Rotterdam in the Netherlands has also come to notice as an entry point

for cocaine concealed in commercial shipping containers. Other intelligence suggests that Italy, France and Portugal are also maritime entry points. With the ease of transportation between the UK and mainland Europe, it appears that the cocaine consignments are simply split into small quantities, usually under 20 kg, and driven through the Channel Tunnel or imported on ferries or commercial airlines. Finally, there have been occurrences, albeit rare, of boats transporting large quantities of cocaine direct from South America to the UK.

A variety of methods of smuggling cocaine have been observed. These include concealment amongst clothing, perishable goods, on commercial airlines to be retrieved later, and concealed in other equipment. The use of couriers travelling on commercial airlines is common, particularly by West Indian and West African criminals. Methods include internal concealment, body belts and hard-sided suitcases. Frequent small importations mean that quantities can quickly mount.

Warehousing

Most intelligence suggests that warehousing tends to occur on a European-wide scale rather than within the UK itself – mainly in Spain, the Netherlands and Eastern Europe. In most cases, buyers have been arranged prior to the arrival of the shipment, so that long-term warehousing is not an issue. Recent intelligence indicates that the cocaine market is very fluid and that, in the main, importers and distributors are anxious for shipments to leave their hands as soon as possible.

Distribution

Most cocaine entering the UK mainland will be consumed here, and it is believed that with usage on the increase, cocaine is now more available than at any time in the past. It is assessed that, between them,

South American groups and British crime families represent the most serious threat in the cocaine market. A number of Colombian traffickers in the UK are actively importing cocaine and subsequently distributing it wholesale on behalf of both large organisations based in Colombia and themselves. The British and South American groups appear to be the only ones who move large shipments into the UK; most of the other seizures were for amounts of a few kilograms. It is, however, believed that British crime families are responsible for the greatest volume of cocaine distribution within the UK. The main distribution hubs in the UK are London, Liverpool, Manchester, Birmingham, Bradford, Bristol and Glasgow. The distribution links are similar to those for heroin, though the supply side of the market is somewhat more fragmented.

Synthetics

The synthetic drug market is possibly the most rapidly expanding drug market in the UK. Since synthetic drugs can be manufactured from chemicals, there is no need to have access to raw materials such as coca or opium to be a major first-level supplier. As a result, the synthetic drug market is different from both the cocaine and heroin markets. While it is possible to synthesise versions of drugs such as heroin or cocaine, the ready availability of plant-based drugs means that such synthesis is, at present, not viable. The synthetic drugs are all part of the same family of drugs commonly known as amphetamine-type stimulants (ATS). The group is itself broken down into two further subgroups: those drugs closely related to amphetamine itself such as methyl amphetamine, and the ring substituted phenethylamines commonly known as ecstasy-type drugs.

Synthetics for the UK market are almost exclusively manufactured either in the UK itself or on the near continent. Ten to 20% is manufactured in the UK. The rest is believed to be manufactured on the near continent, primarily the Netherlands and Belgium. Manufacturing is increasing, particularly

in Eastern Europe. However, at present, production from these other sources does not appear to have reached the UK in significant quantities.

Importation

As synthetic drugs destined for the UK market are manufactured on the near continent (the Netherlands and Belgium), importation is relatively easy for the traffickers. The Channel ports are an obvious route, as are the UK's many airports. The size and diverse nature of the market both within the UK and in Europe mean that, in addition to the involvement of large, organised crime groups in trafficking, a number of smaller, entrepreneurial traffickers also contribute to a significant proportion of the supply market.

During 1999, significant changes to the pattern of importation were detected. Essentially, fewer shipments were seized but these shipments were increasing in size. The smaller-scale shipments from entrepreneurial importers, whilst not disappearing entirely, declined significantly whilst larger-scale

seizures, presumably from organised crime groups, were on the increase.

Whilst this change in the pattern of shipments was occurring, other changes in the market were also happening. The price differential between synthetic drugs in the UK and the Netherlands – most significantly at the wholesale point – was narrowing considerably. This may be as a result of a small number of distributors monopolising importation of the drug from the Netherlands, and subsequent wholesale supply. In addition, synthetic drugs were increasingly being seized as part of multi-drug shipments, including quite significant quantities of both heroin and cocaine.

Manufacturing within the UK

Production in the UK consists of both relatively small-scale laboratories which are capable of producing significant amounts of drugs, as well as large-scale laboratories which have significant output. While small-scale laboratories can be set up by various kinds of criminal organisations, from the relatively inexperienced to the

Drug-related deaths

England and Wales, Scotland and Northern Ireland 1990-1999

Year	England and Wales		Scotland		Northern Ireland	
	Number	Male-female ratio	Number	Male-female ratio	Number	Male-female ratio
1990	2041	1.3	–	–	39	0.6
1991	2053	1.4	–	–	46	0.6
1992	2287	1.4	–	–	28	0.9
1993	2252	1.5	–	–	28	0.8
1994	2404	1.7	422	1.6	35	1.3
1995	2563	1.8	426	1.7	46	1.3
1996	2721	2.0	460	2.2	40	1.1
1997	2858	2.1	447	1.8	39	1.0
1998	2922	2.0	449	2.1	40	1.5
1999	–	–	492	2.3	50	2.3

sophisticated organised crime groups, large-scale laboratories require expertise in a number of areas including the ability to distribute a sizeable amount of drugs.

Warehousing

The issue of stockpiling is slightly different in the synthetic drugs market. Most of the large-scale laboratories in the Netherlands and Belgium are believed to manufacture according to regular orders from organised crime groups. Since an established manufacturing and tableting operation can produce a final product in a very short time-scale, there is no need to stockpile an end product.

Distribution

London and Liverpool are identified as the principal cities which supply most of the UK synthetic drug market. Although this appears to be similar to the distribution patterns for heroin and cocaine, there is only a limited amount of data available and it has been difficult to draw firm conclusions. Despite this, however, it is assessed that there is a general distribution pattern involving organised crime which cuts across all drug types.

Conclusions

There appears to be a convergence in the various drug markets. Many criminal groups are specialising in segments of the market, not in one

> *The ease with which organised crime groups can set up illegal laboratories suggests that the production of these types of drugs will increase as long as the market exists*

drug type but in providing particular services such as transportation. Generally speaking, the phenomenon of poly-drug use has been growing amongst users for some time and it is likely that multi-drug supply will develop throughout all levels of the supply network.

As the major suppliers of drugs continue to develop links with British criminals to widen the distribution of their products and supply the poly-drug culture, one may observe a higher level of co-operation amongst the traffickers and sellers. Such networking improves availability, combats the efforts of law enforcement and can maximise profits.

Criminals will continue to examine the successes and failures in trafficking their illegal commodities and change their operations accordingly whether by altering routes, devising new methods of concealment or recruiting new couriers.

The implementation and con-

tinued application of coca crop eradication programmes should eventually have an effect on the overall levels of cocaine production. However, observable decreases will only become apparent over the next 5 to 10 years. There is every possibility that the criminals based in these areas will foresee this occurrence and take the opportunity to diversify their production strategies. This may be reflected by a relocation of cultivation sites or a movement into other areas of drug production. It is anticipated that the South American production of heroin and synthetic drugs will increase. Organised criminals may seek new markets and reduce their reliance on cocaine. Although South American heroin is primarily shipped to the US market, one may see these criminal groups targeting new markets such as Europe if sufficient yields are produced.

The ease with which organised crime groups can set up illegal laboratories to make amphetamine and methylamphetamine suggests that the production of these types of drugs will increase as long as the market exists. New types of designer drugs, such as ATS, are expected to arrive in the UK. An increase in the production of new designer drugs may be seen as criminals attempt to add new chemical bonds to existing illegal drugs in an effort to subvert legislation.

© National Criminal Intelligence Service (NCIS)

Drugs tsar hails new detector

By Alan Travis, Home Affairs Editor

New equipment which can spot drugs hidden inside a car by detecting particles in the air could soon be used to help stem the illicit trade into Britain, the government's drugs tsar said yesterday.

In an upbeat speech to science academics and teachers, Keith Hellawell said the government's anti-drugs campaign was showing signs of success, with the growth in experimentation among schoolchildren levelling off.

But he stirred controversy when he singled out some families in Britain's Turkish community as being key links in the heroin trade.

Mr Hellawell, speaking at the International Conference for the Association for Science Education, at Surrey University, said new drug detection equipment being developed by Middlesex University would begin trials next month.

'Just before Christmas I saw a demonstration. Equipment such as

this could be an invaluable aid in detecting smuggled drugs in the way carbon dioxide detection is used to examine vehicles suspected of having illegal immigrants concealed in them.'

Mr Hellawell said he was confident that the new technology would be used to intensify Britain's attempts to disrupt the trade in drugs. Other measures already being taken included seconding British experts to Turkey and eastern European countries applying to enter the EU, to target the smugglers.

But his remarks, regarding the heroin trade, that some Turkish families living in Britain were key links in the supply route from the poppy fields of the far east, as importers and money launderers, sparked protests. He said: 'If you have Turkish families, and families of people with those linkages on the supply chain with legitimate bases in this country, then clearly that's the way this system works.

'We have got money laundering taking place in London, very often by legitimate businesses. But we don't

---

'Equipment such as this could be an invaluable aid in detecting smuggled drugs'

---

want to tarnish all Turkish people or people from eastern Europe as potential criminals. They are not, but these linkages are something that we look at.'

Fulden Cetin, a London-based Turkish radio journalist, said yesterday that Mr Hellawell was wrong to

single out the Turkish community.

Demand in Europe for heroin from the east caused the smugglers to seek a way through. 'Turkey is the easiest route because of its geographical situation. We don't like it either,' he said, urging Britain to step up its help in breaking up drugs mafias.

On a more positive note, Mr Hellawell pointed to a rise in the quantity of drugs detected, a fall in reoffending by addicts who had completed rehabilitation programmes, and more drugs education lessons in schools, as evidence that the government's policy was having an impact.

© Guardian Newspapers Limited 2001

Getting into trouble with drugs

Information from Gary Hayes, DrugScope

At college

Unfortunately even today, some colleges and universities take alarmist approaches to drug use and will do all in their powers to be seen 'stamping out' drug use. This often means dismissing those students found or suspected of using drugs.

Each college has its own policies and practices so we are unable to give you comprehensive guidelines on what to expect. Some staff in student services may be better than others so it's best to check with the students' union first before seeking help for yourself or a friend through the college.

Having drugs for your own use is one thing, but supplying drugs to others is quite another. The law doesn't differentiate between buying a little extra to sell on to a few friends and dealing more widely. Colleges and universities will also take any dealing seriously, many will take punitive action even where very small amounts of a drug are involved. One course of action is to refuse student accommodation to those suspected or found dealing, growing or producing on the premises. Carrying out any of these activities in your student flat has consequences not only for yourself, but also on your flat mates and the college

renting out the flat. Be aware that some colleges will always involve the police if they believe criminal activity is taking place either in your student flat or on campus.

The police and the law

Caution
This is a complex area where we can only provide general guidelines. Anyone in difficulties with the law should get legal advice at the earliest opportunity by contacting their solicitor or Release on 020 7603 8654 (24 hours).

The Misuse of Drugs Act
The main law controlling the use of drugs is the Misuse of Drugs Act. It divides drugs into three classes, A-C. Class A drugs are regarded as the most dangerous and so carry the heaviest penalties.

Having drugs for your own use is one thing, but supplying drugs to others is quite another

---

The drugs

Class A drugs: cocaine and crack, ecstasy, heroin, methadone, processed magic mushrooms, LSD.

Class B drugs: amphetamine, cannabis resin and herb, codeine phosphate and some other strong painkillers.

Class C drugs: steroids and tranquillisers (supply is the main offence here).

Magic mushrooms: It is not an offence to possess magic mushrooms in their natural state. However, psilocin and psilocybin, the drugs that they contain, are Class A drugs. So if the mushrooms are intentionally prepared by, for example, drying, freezing or pickling, then you might be charged with possession, supply, intent to supply or even production.

The main offences
The most common offence is possession of a controlled drug. This includes joint possession of a common pool of drugs and past possession, when past drug use is admitted. There is no offence if you are found with a drug you didn't know was there (e.g. if a friend put it in your pocket) but you might have to prove this in court. More serious offences are supply and intention to

supply. Remember, supply includes giving or selling drugs to a friend, or even looking after them for someone else. People who say, 'the drugs were not all for me, some were for a friend' usually make things worse for themselves by admitting supply. The heaviest penalties under the law concern the import and supply of controlled drugs.

Making or growing your own
Cultivation of cannabis is also an offence. Penalties are more severe if the court believes cultivation was intended to supply others. It is not an offence to possess cannabis seeds.

Manufacturing illegal drugs will be dealt with severely, usually in excess of what is given out for supply. Some drugs which are not illegal to possess such as Ketamine, GHB, herbal ecstasy, or poppers are covered by the Medicines Act 1968 which means that it is illegal to manufacture or sell such drugs without proper authorisation.

Prosecution and punishment
There are numerous factors to take into account in determining the likely punishment for any particular offence. Different police forces have their own approach to drug offences. Whilst some will caution for first-time offenders, others will always prosecute. There are also variations depending on whether the case is tried by a Magistrates' Court or a Crown Court, who deal out the heavier punishments. The maximum penalties can be summarised as follows:

Possession	Supply
Class A drug	
7 years + fine	Life + fine
Class B drug	
5 years + fine	14 years + fine
Class C drug	
2 years + fine	5 years + fine

In reality maximum sentences are rarely imposed, usually only for repeat offenders involved in serious offences. Many aggravating and mitigating factors can operate, such as the amount of the drug involved, whether it was a first offence or not and the defendant's character. As a general rule for supply-type offences you will normally be sent to prison. For a simple possession offence you will tend to get a non-custodial sentence.

Seizures of controlled drugs

Seizures of controlled drugs and persons found guilty, cautioned, given a fiscal fine or dealt with by compounding: a summary of main trends (%)

	1988	1989	1990	1991	1992	1993	1994	1995	1996	1997	1998
Total number of which:	100%	100%	100%	100%	100%	100%	100%	100%	100%	100%	100%
Cannabis	87	86	87	85	80	80	82	80	75	77	75
Amphetamines	9	6	8	10	15	13	12	13	15	13	13
Heroin	6	5	4	4	4	4	4	6	8	9	10
Cocaine (exc. crack)	2	4	3	3	3	3	3	3	3	3	3
LSD	1	2	3	2	3	3	2	1	1	1	0
Ecstasy-type (1)	-	-	1	2	3	3	3	5	5	4	3

1 MDMA only prior to 1996.

Source: Home Office

Drugs and driving
Under the Road Traffic Act 1988 it is an offence to drive or be in charge of a motor vehicle when unfit through drugs. If guilty of driving when unfit, there's an obligatory 12 months' disqualification and a fine; often longer periods are imposed. In cases involving accidents or other aggravating circumstances, then longer disqualifications, stiffer fines and imprisonment can apply. It is also an offence to be drunk whilst in charge of a vehicle (even just sleeping it off in your car!).

Your rights
You can be stopped and searched if the police have reasonable suspicion that you are in possession of a controlled drug. They cannot carry out an intimate search or remove hats or outer clothing in public view.

Remember: in a police station you have the right to be treated humanely and with respect; to know why you have been arrested; to speak to the custody officer; to have someone notified of your arrest; to consult with your own solicitor or the duty solicitor privately; to speak to Release who will put you in contact

---

Different police forces have their own approach to drug offences. Whilst some will caution for first time offenders, others will always prosecute

---

with a lawyer. These rights can sometimes be delayed, but no one can refuse them.

Employment
Having a record
If you have been prosecuted for any offence, this will be stored on a police database, referred to as your criminal record. Having a record, and in particular for something drug related, will put off many employers.

Many professions automatically exclude individuals with past convictions related to drugs, these include in particular the judicial, medical sectors, and professions working with children. If you don't reveal your record and the employer finds out later, you will almost certainly be sacked. After a period of time, some convictions are 'spent' and do not have to be disclosed. Some jobs are exempt from this. Getting caught therefore with an illegal drug on you can damage many study and career ambitions. So bear this in mind if you come in contact with drugs.

Drug testing
If you are going for a job interview, you may face a drug test, even if the job has nothing to do with public safety. The police and Armed Services usually drug test new recruits, as well as some commercial companies. Most tests involve taking a sample of urine. Drugs will stay in the system for some time after you have taken them. How long that will be is different for every drug and will also depend on many other factors like individual metabolism. So what follows is only a very rough guide.

Drug	Detection periods in urine
Alcohol	12-24 hours
Amphetamine	2-4 days
Cannabis	30 days for heavy use
Cocaine/crack	12 hrs – 3 days
Dia-/Temazepam	1-2 days
Ecstasy	2-4 days
Heroin	1-2 days
LSD	2-3 days
Methadone	2 days

Traces of drug use can also be found on body hair: the longer the hair, the more drug history can be revealed. This method of testing is proving increasingly popular with, for example, the police.

Drugs and travelling abroad

If you are travelling abroad it is important to know the laws regarding drugs in the different countries you may visit as well as the laws in the UK on your return. A common misconception is that drugs bought legally in one country can be carried to another country. Cannabis or mushrooms bought in Holland for example cannot be brought into most other European countries. If you have some drugs left after a visit, do not try to take them out with you for the sake of a few guilders or pesetas – get rid of them. Scandinavian countries in particular have greater restrictions on imports and exclude some medicines and herbal remedies such as Khat and even codeine linctus. Outside Europe a number of countries do not take kindly to people bringing in illegal substances and threaten the death penalty to those found guilty of drug trafficking. Therefore, before you set off, find out what medication or other drugs you can and can't take with you. The national embassies in London are a good source of information.

• The above information is from DrugScope. See page 41 for their address details. © DrugScope

Crack down on drugs

Met rat catchers are back

Metropolitan Police Service Commissioner Sir John Stevens pledged that there would be no let-up in the Met's determination to crack down on drug dealers in the capital as he launched the Met's 'Rat on a Rat' advertising campaign for 2001.

The Commissioner also revealed that thanks to calls made to the Crimestoppers number by members of the public, drugs with an estimated street value of £27,144,491 had been seized by police in London last year.

This advertising campaign, which supports Operation Crack Down, the Met's anti-drugs initiative, follows a similar drive in 1999, which caught the public's imagination and helped generate more than 2,000 calls to the Crimestoppers' Unit at New Scotland Yard. The information gathered from the advertising campaign will assist operational police activity in targeting drug dealers and those who supply dealers.

Sir John said: 'Drug dealing at street level impinges on the quality of life for people in local neighbourhoods. Last year's "Rat on a Rat" advertising campaign clearly displayed the public's determination and drive to assist police in ridding the streets of these criminals. I hope that this year's initiative will prove just as successful and I would ask communities to continue to work with us by phoning Crimestoppers anonymously with drug intelligence.'

He added: 'We have just finished simultaneous drug enforcement operations in 10 London boroughs and have charged 300 people with drug-related offences. The research findings from the recent activity will assist in shaping and informing the Met's drugs enforcement strategy in the future. Officers will act on intelligence received through the initiative as well as on information

already received following the recent Operation Crack Down activity.'

Rt Hon Tony Blair, Prime Minister, offered his support to the campaign and said:

'We have all seen how the abuse of drugs like crack cocaine eats away at our society bringing misery and destroying lives. It is everyone's responsibility to tackle this problem and I fully support the Met in re-running the "Rat on a Rat" campaign. Last year's campaign was very successful in encouraging members of the public to work with the police to tackle the scourge of drugs and I wish this campaign every success.'

The 'Rat on a Rat' message will be displayed on perimeter fence panels at football stadia, in football programmes and on roadside poster sites. Posters will also be displayed in washrooms at pubs and clubs and on beermats. Local press, ethnic press and radio stations will also be targeted by the campaign.

The latest statistics from Crimestoppers for the period of January – December 2000 reveal that the unit took 1044 actionable calls from members of the public about drugs. These calls lead to 300 arrests and the recovery of £27,144,491 worth of drugs. **Drug dealers ruin lives. Call Crimestoppers anonymously.**

© Metropolitan Police Service

High time for a decent debate

Phillip Oppenheim has his drug of choice (alcohol). Should the state prevent other people using theirs?

OK, I'll admit it. I take drugs. I deal in them too. How's that for confessional-chic? I run a bar which shakes out around 1,000 highly alcoholic cocktails a week. Mind you, I never use that other stuff, cannabis. However, once I enjoyed a bit of passive smoking in Moscow where an innocent friend had gone to work as a lawyer.

Clients had introduced him to the seductive delights of marijuana. So impressed was he that he decided to buy his own. 'How much?' gruffed the Kazakh dealer down the crackly line. 'Ooh, $100,' replied my friend, unsure of what to say. He heard a gasp and the line clicked dead. Two days later there was a knock at the door of his apartment. There stood three swarthy Kazakhs, grinning like new Labour politicians, humping bin liners full of grass.

Unsure what to do with it all, my friend filled the empty window boxes of his balcony overlooking the courtyard. A couple of weeks later he held a dinner for friends while I was visiting and put candles in the window boxes. After a spot of clubbing we returned to find the block wreathed in a sweet-smelling haze. Like our great leaders, I tried not to inhale. But for days afterwards, ancient Soviet matrons living in the block went around making peace signs and blowing kisses.

Not that it would have done the old girls much harm. Many medics would say that my drug, alcohol, is more dangerous than cannabis. Yet we are behind many other countries in our attitudes. Decriminalisation of cannabis is under way in Spain, Portugal, Switzerland and France. Prosecutions are rare in Austria, Germany and Denmark. Ireland issues only fines. Limited decriminalisation has been in place in the Netherlands

By Phillip Oppenheim

for years. Here, we jail about 2,500 people a year for minor cannabis offences at a cost of around £100m in hard-earned cigarette taxes.

Perhaps we should return to Victorian values. Cannabis reached Britain in the 1840s and was widely prescribed as a medicine. Queen Victoria used cannabis – and opium – to ease period pains. The drug was legal in Britain and the US until the 1920s. Ever since, drug penalties have become more and more severe and massive sums are spent on enforcement. The result? We had 2,000 heroin addicts in 1980: now there are 200,000. The British Crime Survey suggests that nearly half of 16- to 29-year-olds in London take coke. A Mori report showed that 69% of students at Manchester admitted to using drugs – only 46% had sex once a week, which shows some worrying priorities among our young people. Tougher penalties, greater enforcement, more users. You might have thought that someone

would twig that something is wrong.

We are getting the rottenest of all worlds. Criminalising drugs hands massive profits to organised crime. According to the UN, criminal gangs make more than Britain's GNP. Their main product? Drugs. Colombia now counts cocaine farming in its official figures. Interpol estimates the drugs trade at £350bn a year – more than cars and about the same as oil.

That's just the big guys. Addicts need around £400 a week to finance their habit – and they don't all make it staring at screens in the City. Most thieve £1,200-worth of CDs and laptops to pay for their drugs.

Despite the huge resources of the state they mostly get away with it. Not long after my passive smoking incident I found myself as a Treasury minister in charge of customs and excise. I was shown a huge warehouse in Dover, stacked high with aromatic bales and bags of white powder. 'We snaffle about 1% of what goes through, I reckon,' said the customs man.

I was also privileged to meet Snout, top sniffer dog, a mutt of

uncertain lineage but noble features. Snout operates at Heathrow where a demonstration of his detective skills was put on. He soon whiffed out the bag planted on an officer. Snout's reward was his favourite toy. Our reward is to spend £1.4bn directly on drugs, two-thirds of which goes to the courts and prison. Just one-third goes on treatment.

Illegality doesn't eliminate drugs, it merely drives them underground where they nurture crime, just as in the US where homicides rose rapidly after 1910 when states began to go dry. After Prohibition ended in 1934 the murder rate fell again, increasing only in the late 50s as the illegal drugs trade grew.

Not that drugs are not harmful. Clearly they are. Try listening to anyone after a couple of spliffs. Cocaine has the harmful social quality that it deludes people into thinking they can dance. All drugs levy their price. But in an imperfect world, legalisation looks like the lesser evil. It would deprive organised crime of a lush franchise, it would put a stop to much petty crime, it would reduce enforcement costs, end the problem of impure drugs and make users more accessible for treatment. One other advantage: legalised cannabis could be taxed – the ultimate stealth tax – but please, Gordon, not so high that it would encourage smuggling. The proceeds could go to educating people and treatment.

Criminalisation does not work. But there is a broader issue: to what extent should the state prevent people from doing what does not impinge on others?

Both of the two main parties need some lateral mind expansion on the subject. New Labour, in its desperation to suck up to *Daily Mail* England, slapped Mo Mowlam down when she admitted her marijuana moment. Their contribution to the debate is a drugs tsar and, of course, targets.

At least the dopey Ann Widdecombe began a debate among the Tories which has become part of a larger current. The new punch-up is between social authoritarians and social liberals, who argue that the state should stay out of both our economic and personal lives. 'You'd rather take a shower with Norman Bates than put Widders in charge of social policy,' said one libertarian MP. In a few short days William Hague has shuffled from being 'right behind' his shadow home secretary to calling for a national debate on drugs. It's a shame he was not far-sighted enough to do that in the first place. He might have been surprised by the reaction. We need the debate. Don't, though, expect some fluffy, holistic consensus.

It's a 'three-pipe problem' worthy of the great sniffer-dog himself, cocaine-fancier Sherlock Holmes. There are uncomfortable questions ahead. Do we decriminalise cannabis use, leaving supply in the hands of criminals, or legalise, regulate and tax? Where do we draw the line? Ecstasy? Cocaine? Would legal, but heavily regulated harder drugs also be the lesser evil? Is legalisation in one country feasible? One thing is sure: the drugs policy doesn't work. Give Snout and his toy a well-deserved holiday. As for drug tsars, well, we know how tsars end up.

• As Conservative Treasury minister in charge of customs and excise, Phillip Oppenheim served on a government committee on drugs in 1996-97.

Cannabis research: a story of highs and lows

By Lee Elliot Major

The scientific case for decriminalising cannabis for medicinal use remains inconclusive. Research hitting the headlines during December has highlighted the downs as well as highs of taking marijuana.

A serious blow came when researchers at New Zealand's Asthma and Respiratory Foundation scotched claims that the drug is less harmful than tobacco. The Otago University academics found that smoking cannabis five times a week does as much lung damage as smoking 20 cigarettes a day. The project concluded that smoking cannabis 'caused disease, phlegm and coughing fits' – after scrutinising the lungs of 943 people aged 21.

But then clinical trials at an East Anglian hospital brought fresh hope for the campaign to legalise the drug which was recommended for the treatment of constipation, gout, malaria, rheumatism and menstrual problems by the Chinese as long ago as 2800 BC. Ten out of 13 multiple sclerosis sufferers reported significant relief from pain, in a small-scale trial at the James Paget Hospital, in Norfolk.

More highs were to come. Aberdeen University scientists announced they had developed a new method for making cannabis soluble for the first time. The technique could mean that cannabis is one day delivered in sprays, aerosols or injections, consigning the need for rizlas and tobacco to the ashtray of history.

But before the government could start caving in to the demands to legalise the medicinal use of cannabis, the issue became distinctly hazy again. Marijuana, new research suggested, could become an oral contraceptive for the future. US researchers discovered that consuming marijuana can make sperm sluggish, reducing the chances of having children. (For those trying for babies the research also suggested a good reason for only smoking after, and definitely not before, having sex.)

The scientists from University Buffalo, New York State, identified chemicals in the drug which can overload an important signalling system in the brain involved in fertility. When consumed by men or women, marijuana can reduce the chances of sperm breaking through the surface of an egg and hinder the development of a newly-fertilised embryo.

Steering ability of another kind is also impaired by smoking cannabis, according to research at the UK

Whatever the hazards of the drug, those using cannabis for medicinal purposes at least appear to have won the popular vote

---

Transport Research Laboratory . The drug makes people drive badly – but less so than alcohol or fatigue, the experiment found. Volunteers drove more slowly and cautiously while under the influence of cannabis, but

---

their steering ability was badly affected. And volunteers found it particularly difficult to follow a figure-of-eight loop road when given a high dose.

But whatever the hazards of the drug, those using cannabis for medicinal purposes at least appear to have won the popular vote. An ICM poll carried out for the *Guardian* revealed that 71% of people supported the proposition that the Metropolitan Police should be persuaded to take no action against the medicinal use of cannabis. Only 48% supported this in April 2000.

Majority regard cannabis as no worse than drink

By Alan Travis

Aclear majority of British voters believe that using cannabis is no worse than smoking or drinking, according to the latest *Guardian*/ICM opinion poll.

The survey also shows that the overwhelming majority also believe that smoking dope should not remain a criminal act in Britain. Some 43% even go so far as saying that its personal use should be legalised completely – a far higher proportion than previously recorded on *Guardian*/ICM opinion polls.

The findings confirm the view that a change has taken place in British public opinion about the future legal status of cannabis and that Ann Widdecombe was out of tune when she proposed replacing a policy of police cautions with a mandatory £100 fixed-penalty fine. Only one in five voters believes that possession of cannabis should remain a criminal offence.

Opinion is most pro-cannabis among the 25 to 34 age group, some 50% of whom believe its personal use should be legalised. Two-thirds of this age group believe that smoking cannabis is no worse than smoking tobacco or drinking alcohol. This is higher than even the 65% of 18-24-year-olds who subscribe to the same view. Indeed, the only age group to disagree with this proposition is the

over-65s, some 49% of whom were against. Even among these 'grey voters' one in three agrees that cannabis is no worse than alcohol or tobacco.

Despite the fact that politicians in recent days have contrasted the experience of middle-class youngsters at university with what goes on in 'the real world' of inner-city council estates, there is little difference in view across social class about cannabis law reform. Some 45% of DE voters – the unskilled and unemployed – think it should be legalised as do 44% of AB voters – the professional classes.

The poll does however show a clear divide between those who want to see the decriminalisation of cannabis but are not yet prepared to see it fully legalised. While 22% said they believed the personal use of cannabis should remain a criminal act, some 30% said the police should not make prosecution a priority and it should effectively be decriminalised. The issue has polarised opinion with only 4% of voters saying they had no opinion on the matter.

The findings of this poll, combined with weekend surveys also showing large majorities for decriminalisation, will put Tony Blair and Jack Straw under further pressure to reassess the government's policy on drugs.

The next opportunity will come when Home Office ministers give evidence to the Commons home affairs select committee on why they dismissed within hours of publication the Police Foundation report on cannabis published in March. The report, which included two chief constables among its membership, recommended that prison should no longer be used for cannabis possession.

Some 4,500 people were imprisoned last year after being convicted of cannabis charges.

Ten reasons to legalise drugs

Information from Transform – the campaign for effective drug policy

1. Address the real issues

For too long policy-makers have used prohibition as a smoke-screen to avoid addressing the social and economic factors that lead people to use drugs. Most illegal and legal drug use is recreational. Poverty and despair are at the root of most problematic drug use and it is only by addressing these underlying causes that we can hope to significantly decrease the number of problematic users.

2. Eliminate the criminal market place

The market for drugs is demand-led and millions of people demand illegal drugs. Making the production, supply and use of these drugs illegal creates a vacuum into which organised crime moves. The illegal trade is dirty, dangerous and worth billions of pounds.

Legalisation forces organised crime from the drugs trade, starves them of income and enables us to regulate and control the market (i.e. prescription, licensing, laws on sales to minors, advertising regulations etc.).

3. Massively reduce crime

The price of illegal drugs is determined by a demand-led, unregulated market. Using illegal drugs is very expensive. This means that some dependent users resort to stealing to raise funds. Most of the violence associated with illegal drug dealing is caused by its illegality.

Half of all UK property crime is drug related – £2 billion a year.

Legalisation would enable us to regulate the market, determine a much lower price and remove users' need to raise funds through crime. Our legal system would be freed up and our prison population dramatically reduced, saving billions. Although most tobacco smokers are dependent addicts, they do not have to steal to support their habits.

WHAT'S THE PRICE OF ILLEGAL DRUGS?

...ABOUT £2 BILLION... NOT TO MENTION LIVES, FAMILIES AND FUTURES..

4. Drug users are a majority

How many people neither drink nor smoke? Recent research shows that nearly half of all 15-16-year-olds have used an illegal drug. Up to one and a half million people use ecstasy every weekend. Amongst young people, illegal drug use is seen as normal. Intensifying the 'war on drugs' is not reducing demand. In Holland, where cannabis laws are far less harsh, drug usage is amongst the lowest in Europe.

'If the [drug] problem continues advancing as it is at the moment, we're going to be faced with some very frightening options. Either you have a massive reduction in civil rights or you have to look at some radical solutions. The issue has to be, Can a criminal justice system solve this particular problem?' Commander John Grieve, Criminal Intelligence Unit, Scotland Yard, 1997.

Legalisation accepts that drug use is normal and that it is a social issue, not a criminal justice one. We could begin by prescribing heroin to addicts.

5. Provide access to truthful information and education

A wealth of disinformation about drugs and drug use is given to us by ignorant and prejudiced policy-makers and media who peddle myths upon lies for their own ends. This creates many of the risks and dangers associated with drug use.

Legalisation would help us to disseminate open, honest and truthful information to users and non-users to help them to make decisions about whether and how to use. We could begin research again on presently illicit drugs to discover all their uses and effects – both positive and negative.

6. Global implications

The illegal drugs market makes up 8% of all world trade (around £300 billion a year). Whole countries are run under the corrupting influence of drug cartels. Prohibition also enables developed countries to wield vast political power over producer nations under the auspices of drug control programmes.

Legalisation returns lost revenue

to the legitimate taxed economy and removes some of the high-level corruption. It also removes a tool of political interference by foreign countries against producer nations.

7. Restore our rights and responsibilities

Prohibition unnecessarily criminalises millions of otherwise law-abiding people. It removes the responsibility for distribution of drugs from policy-makers and hands it over to un-regulated, sometimes violent dealers.

Legalisation restores our right to use drugs responsibly to change the way we think and feel. It enables controls and regulations to be put in place to protect the vulnerable.

8. Black rights and the criminal justice system

Black people are over ten times more likely to be imprisoned for drug offences than whites. Arrests for drug offences are notoriously discretionary, allowing enforcement to easily target a particular ethnic group. Prohibition has fostered this stereotyping of black people.

Legalisation removes a whole set of laws that are used to disproportionately bring black people into contact with the criminal justice system. It would help to redress the over-representation of black drug offenders in prison.

9. Make all drug use safer

Prohibition has led to the stigmatisation and marginalisation of drug users. Countries that operate ultra-prohibitionist policies have very high rates of HIV infection amongst injecting users. Hepatitis C rates amongst users in the UK are increasing substantially.

In the UK in the 80s clean needles for injecting users and safer sex education for young people were made available in response to fears of HIV. Harm reduction policies are in direct opposition to prohibitionist laws.

10. Prohibition doesn't work

There is no evidence to show that prohibition is succeeding. The question we must ask ourselves is, 'What are the benefits of criminalising any drug?' If, after examining all the available evidence, we find that the costs outweigh the benefits, then we must seek an alternative policy.

Legalisation is not a cure-all but it does allow us to address many of the problems associated with drug use, and those created by prohibition. The time has come for an effective and pragmatic drug policy.

Transformation and re-evaluation
Transform is a national organisation campaigning for reform of drug policy and legislation. We are campaigning for effective policy regarding all drugs – illegal, prescription, over the counter and licensed retail drugs. We aim to build a mass movement of activists who will engage in activities to campaign for effective change. We believe that:

The so-called 'war on drugs' is a war against people. It has been lost.

Prohibition is failing to deliver any of the outcomes we all seek. It is time to replace prohibition with an effective and all-encompassing strategy that will enable us to regulate and control the market. This transformation will be phased in over a number of years. It will involve extensive research and pilot studies. It will be based on pragmatism not dogma and will involve all concerned agencies.

Huge amounts of money spent fighting the war on drugs could be far better spent on education and treatment, or in fact virtually anything else.

The distinction between 'hard' and 'soft' drugs is pointless and misleading. We must look at the whole range of effects of each drug to decide what action to take.

• See page 41 for their address details.

© *Transform*

Belgium legalises personal pot use

By Andrew Osborn in Brussels

Governments in Europe are about to come under renewed pressure to decriminalise cannabis after Belgium's decision to legalise the personal use of *le hasch* for anyone over the age of 18.

Under radical plans approved by the cabinet on Friday, it will soon be legal to grow, import and consume potentially unlimited amounts of pot for personal use in Belgium.

'Any possession of cannabis for personal consumption will no longer provoke a reaction from the justice system unless its use is considered to be problematic or creates a social nuisance,' the health minister, Magda Aelvoet, said.

However, it will still be against the law to deal in or supply cannabis, or to produce the drug in industrial quantities for sale. Nor will Belgium replicate the Netherlands' fabled network of coffee shops selling cannabis cigarettes over the counter. Hard drugs will continue to be outlawed.

Italy, Spain and Portugal are reported to be considering similar moves for cannabis and Belgium's decision to relax its laws will make the British government, which has repeatedly refused to consider decriminalisation, look increasingly isolated.

It has been legal since 1976 to buy and use cannabis in any one of the Netherlands' 1,500 coffee shops. Within a few months, Belgium will become the second country in the EU to follow suit when it amends its own drugs laws, which date back to 1921.

In Britain, the government has stated that it will reject calls to decriminalise cannabis despite a report from the Police Foundation recommending more relaxed penalties for its use and medical evidence that the drug eases chronic pain.

Controversially, the Belgian government has said it will not define what constitutes a reasonable amount of pot, leaving it up to the country's judiciary to set the legal precedent.

© *Guardian Newspapers Limited 2001*

Don't make a hash of your life

Cannabis is neither soft nor safe

Grass, weed, draw, ganja, blow, marijuana and hash

Whatever name you choose to use, whatever way you use it, this substance will do you no good.

'Come on, get real, none of my friends have died from using it.'

OK, but there are other ways in which you can permanently harm your life.

'Like what? I'm told it's safer than cigarettes or alcohol.'

No! Cannabis is actually a very powerful drug that is able to muddle the brain.

'Go on then, give me some facts, let's hear the evidence.'

The cannabis plant is a type of Indian hemp – its leaves and flower tops are dried (Marijuana – Grass). Cannabis resin is brown and looks like an 'Oxo' cube and from this a treacly liquid (oil) can be extracted. The main active ingredient is THC.* In some respects, a more powerful drug than alcohol and more difficult to flush out of the body.

'Do I have to go through a science lesson?'

If you understand how this drug works you will understand how seriously bad it is.

I'll continue – its effects will depend on whether it is smoked or eaten, but will generally last from 1 to 3 hours – you may feel relaxed – talkative – even have a mild hallucination.

'Great, sounds really cool – so where's the snag?'

Well firstly, you could feel sick, depressed, anxious, confused or even paranoid and have a panic attack.

'Oh.'

And ... riding a bike, driving a car or even crossing the street could be dangerous to you and others.

'OK, so I'll smoke at home or find a nice quiet place.'

That solves nothing – long-term using could still be a total disaster.

'Why?'

That's because THC is stored in fatty tissue in the body and the brain contains a high proportion of fat. That means it can affect your mental processes for several weeks after using.

'Affect me how?'

- Problems with remembering ... even the last thing you've said.
- Inability to concentrate for long on anything.
- Lethargy – you just can't be bothered.
- Delusions about your ability.
- You will know something is wrong in your head but you won't know why!
- You can lose your sense of judgement and fail to recognise that something is dangerous.

'Is there more?'

Oh yes, inhibitions can go out of the window leading to crime, unwanted pregnancy or even buying and taking other drugs while semi-stoned.

So over time, you can become unreliable, irresponsible, apathetic, even careless with little motivation for anything except dope – that could affect school work performance, your job and social life. You start to lose control in every area of your life.

In the acute stages you could develop Cannabis Psychosis.

'What's that?'

You will be going mad but you won't realise it is actually happening.

'Excuse me interrupting, but if I have already started using cannabis surely all I have to do is stop?'

That's the theory, but whilst cannabis is not physically addictive, it most certainly is psychologically. This could mean that when you stop using, sleep could be difficult, you could feel irritable, moody and with no appetite ... not pleasant.

It is better not to start and then you won't be deceived.

'So is there anything else that I should tell my friends?'

There most certainly is. Cannabis doesn't do your body much good either especially if you start really young. Smoking cannabis you have a much higher chance of getting a lung infection, even big C. THC can attack the body's immune system so lowering its resistance to other diseases, and if you have heart problems cannabis can add to the damage.

'Any more good news?'

Yes, cannabis is illegal. It's a class B drug (oil class A) and it is illegal to possess it, to use it or to supply it to others. You could end up in court just because you sold some to a friend to help him out when he felt tense or stressed and then have a police record.

Finally

If you haven't started taking dope – don't

If you have started – stop now! ... and start the recovery process

If you smoke, consider stopping – young people who smoke are much more likely to take illegal drugs+

And ... just to let you know – there is real life without taking drugs.

• If you want to know more contact us. Life for the World Trust, Wakefield Building, Gomm Road, High Wycombe, Bucks HP123 7DJ. Helpline (01494) 462008
*THC Tetrahydrocannabinol
+Spring Harvest Survey 1995

© Life for the World Trust

Improving the quality of the cannabis debate

Defining the different domains

By John Strang, John Witton and Wayne Hall

The policy debate on cannabis has moved back into prominence in Britain and elsewhere after reports of increases in use during the early 1990s and renewed claims about the therapeutic value of marijuana. Rational debate has often been obstructed because the media present a forced choice between two sets of views. One of these constructed views is that cannabis is harmless when used recreationally, is therapeutically useful, and hence should be legalised. The other is that recreational use is harmful to health and that cannabis should continue to be prohibited for recreational or therapeutic purposes.

This oversimplification of the cannabis debate has prevented a more considered examination of eight conceptually separate issues. We believe that a competent consideration of these issues would contribute to a more informed debate about the appropriate public policies that could be adopted towards cannabis use for recreational or therapeutic purposes.

Summary points

- Cannabis use is increasing steadily in many countries and is most prevalent among young people
- The value of the debate on cannabis is seriously diminished by heated contributions that obstruct rational consideration of important public health and policy issues
- The different domains of the debate should be considered in isolation at first to allow a more objective analysis of the evidence
- Substantial public investment in research into the different areas is a prerequisite of rational consideration of public policies

Is cannabis a single product?

More than 60 different cannabinoids and over 400 active components have been identified in samples of cannabis. However, our interest and concerns about associated harms could be much more focused. Should we be especially concerned about the use of new cannabis preparations with higher concentrations of tetrahydrocannabinol? Does using cannabis that has a higher tetrahydrocannabinol content result in a higher intake of tetrahydrocannabinol or do smokers consciously or subconsciously titrate the dose, as do cigarette smokers? What are the rates of dependence and adverse health effects in people who use these more potent forms of cannabis? Tetrahydrocannabinol is the major psychoactive component of cannabis and hence is a logical starting point for search and study.

Uncertainty over harm

The physical harms of regular cannabis use over years and decades have long been a subject of scientific uncertainty. Recent evidence on damage (to the respiratory tract, for example) is rekindling this debate. Now may be an appropriate time for renewed research effort into the effects of long-term cannabis use since sizeable cohorts of long-term users (20 years of use) are now available for study. There is an important supplementary question for these studies, given that tobacco smokers and alcohol consumers often use cannabis. What is the interplay

between the respiratory effects of long-term cannabis and tobacco smoking?

Cannabis and psychological harm

What is the nature of the relation between cannabis and psychosis and other serious psychological harms? How strong is the evidence that cannabis is causally implicated in the precipitation or exacerbation of schizophrenia and other psychoses? Three different clinical conditions need specific consideration.

- To what extent are there time limited, acute psychiatric disturbances such as acute psychosis or panic attacks whose origins may lie in an episode of cannabis use?
- To what extent might cannabis be implicated causally in the genesis of long-term psychiatric disorders that would not otherwise have occurred?
- What weight should be attached to reports that cannabis use adversely affects the course of established mental illnesses for example, precipitating relapses of schizophrenia or manic depressive illness?

Dependence on long-term cannabis use

How important and widespread is dependence on cannabis use? The popular view is that cannabis is not a drug of dependence because it does not have a clearly defined withdrawal syndrome. This is too narrow a view of dependence. Substantial proportions of long-term cannabis users in non-treatment, community samples report that they are dependent; many of them satisfy diagnostic criteria for dependence according to the *Diagnostic and Statistical Manual of Mental Disorders*, third edition, revised and ICD-10 (international classification of diseases, 10th revision) as well as the severity of depression scale; however, fewer consider that they have a cannabis problem. As many as one in 10 cannabis users have been found to want to stop or cut down, find it very difficult to do so, and continue to use cannabis despite the adverse effects that it has on their lives. How serious an impact this type of dependence

has on the lives of affected individuals and their families is unknown, but enough cannabis users have sought treatment to warrant the establishment of local programmes dedicated to quitting.

Domains of the cannabis debate

- What is the importance of the different types of cannabis product composition, presentation, and usage?
- What evidence is there of physical damage from long-term use?
- What evidence is there of psychological or psychiatric (acute and chronic) consequences?
- How widespread is dependence on cannabis and how important is this?
- Is cannabis a 'gateway' drug and what is the importance of this?
- Do some cannabinoids have therapeutic potential and how best can this be used?
- To what extent, and in what ways, is fitness to drive compromised by cannabis use, and for how long?
- What can we learn from experiences with cannabis control policies in other countries?

Is cannabis a 'gateway drug'?

Reuter and MacCoun have examined seven very different ways in which the concept of a gateway drug may be interpreted. Cannabis is typically the first illicit drug that is used by those who subsequently develop problems with heroin and cocaine use. Does cannabis use play a causal role in this sequence of drug involvement? That is the key question for policy, but a difficult one to answer because adolescents who start using cannabis early and become heavy users are found to be independently at higher risk of using other drugs. They are also more likely to keep company with peers who are heavy drug users. If there were a gateway effect, would preventing or delaying the onset of cannabis use (assuming that we could) prevent flow on to other drug use or simply change the sequence of involvement?

Overlooked therapeutic effects?

The cannabinoids are an overlooked group of therapeutic drugs. For over a decade there have been anecdotal and clinical reports on the usefulness of cannabis preparations in treating conditions like nausea, glaucoma, and multiple sclerosis. What conclusions are possible on the evidence to date? What might be learned from better investigation? What implications, if any, do these therapeutic uses have for policies towards recreational cannabis use? The accumulating body of evidence now indicates strongly at least some hitherto uncharted therapeutic applications from some of the more than 60 different cannabinoids or other active products found in samples of the herbal product. However, it is almost certain that new formulations of the relevant (as yet not clearly identified) active components would be required in order to separate any therapeutic effects from harmful effects from smoking the drug. Clinical trials to explore possible therapeutic worth have recently been initiated. As with other medical challenges, disciplined search for active therapeutic ingredients that address health problems which are currently not well managed is now the way forward.

Does cannabis interfere with driving?

To what extent does cannabis use interfere with skilled activities such as driving a motor vehicle or operating machinery? The recognition of the substantial morbidity and mortality caused by drink driving has increased concern about a similar role for illicit drugs in view of the increase in prevalence of use among young adults who are most at risk of accidental injury. Certainly, many drivers stopped by the police or being treated for injuries have been found to have blood or urine samples that test positive for cannabis. However, the importance of these positive toxicological results and their implication for driving competence is not entirely clear. In controlled studies, cannabis has been found to produce impairment. This effect lasts well beyond perceived intoxication, but the full effects seen in controlled research may not occur to the same extent in 'normal' driving on the road because of compensatory responses by drivers who are aware of their impairment. Furthermore, a clearer understanding will be required of the extent to which a particular concentration of the drug (or its metabolites) can reliably be taken as evidence that an individual's driving ability was consequently impaired. Additionally, given the widespread combined use of alcohol and cannabis, it will also be important to establish the effects on accident risk of combining alcohol and cannabis use.

Impact of national policy on cannabis use

What has been the impact of alternative cannabis control policies in different countries on the prevalence of use? It has been difficult confidently to assess the contribution made by different policies. Nevertheless, opportunities do exist for retrospective, or occasionally prospective, studies of the impact of changes in cannabis laws or regulations in individual countries or states. In these studies, adjacent and similar regions are used as quasi-controls to assess the extent to which any observed changes in cannabis use result from the regulatory or legislative change or merely reflect broader trends in society. Careful, objective scrutiny of the available data is only rarely evident. This is hampered by secular increases in cannabis use, the lack of large-scale survey data in countries which have and have not changed their cannabis policies, and the lack of research on the effects of the law as it is applied rather than as expressed in statute.

Rational consideration needed

A more rational consideration of public policies towards cannabis use by adolescents and young adults is urgently required. This is particularly important in view of the evidence of a major increase in cannabis use over the past few decades, the persistence of this substantial level of use, and the continued major law enforcement effort to apprehend cannabis users. Furthermore, doctors need a clearer understanding of the associated adverse health and psychological consequences of acute and chronic use so that they are better able to give appropriate advice to their patients. Substantial public investment in research will be needed to advance our knowledge of the areas outlined above. In its absence, public policy will continue to be made with premature foreclosure of debate in the face of uncertainty by using arbitrary rules about which side in the debate bears the burden of proof – those who defend the status quo or those who wish to reform our cannabis laws. With research, and with greater clarity in each of these domains, we will at last be in a position to formulate evidence-based public policy about cannabis. At the end of the day, the final decisions will, as always, be the outcomes of a political process, but the quality of these decisions would undoubtedly be improved by the availability of better evidence on each of the domains defined above.

Footnotes

Competing interests: A research grant from a private charitable foundation provided part-time employment support for JW while he gathered the available scientific evidence for objective Cochrane-like review. No control over the content of the review is exercised by the fund or any other outside party.

• The above information is an excerpt of the original which appeared in the *British Medical Journal*, January 2000. Visit their web site at www.bmj.com for the entire article.

• John Strang is the Director, and John Witton a research worker of the National Addiction Centre, Institute of Psychiatry, King's College London, London SE5 8AF. Wayne Hall is the Director of the Drug and Alcohol Research Centre, University of New South Wales, Sydney 2052, Australia.

© BMJ 2000

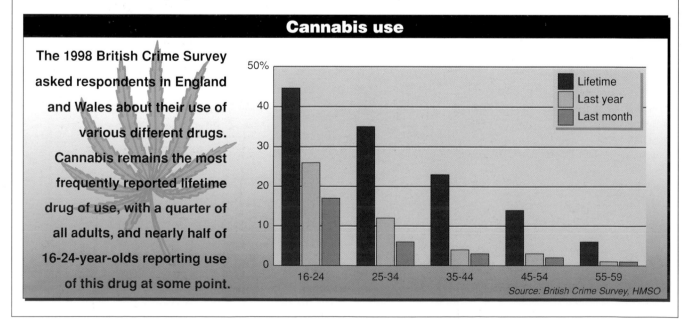

Cannabis use

The 1998 British Crime Survey asked respondents in England and Wales about their use of various different drugs. Cannabis remains the most frequently reported lifetime drug of use, with a quarter of all adults, and nearly half of 16-24-year-olds reporting use of this drug at some point.

Lifetime
Last year
Last month

Source: British Crime Survey, HMSO

Scientists list mental risks from smoking cannabis

By Tim Radford,
Science Editor

Cannabis smoking – besides causing harm to heart, lungs and the immune system – can lead to temporary bouts of mental illness.

Scientists report today in the *British Journal of Psychiatry* that regular use may make things worse for people who have mental health problems, and lead to panic attacks and anxiety in those who do not.

Andrew Johns of the Institute of Psychiatry at the Maudsley hospital in south London surveyed a number of recent studies. One found that 15% of users identified psychotic symptoms or irrational feelings of persecution. Other reports suggested the drug could induce psychosis in people with no history of severe mental illness.

Those with mental illness – living in the community, and as likely as anybody else to get hold of the drug – were even more at risk. 'People with major mental illnesses such as schizophrenia are especially vulnerable, in that cannabis generally provokes relapses and aggravates existing symptoms,' Dr Johns said.

'Health workers need to recognise, and respond to, the adverse effects of cannabis on mental health.'

Researchers are testing cannabis as a potential medicinal drug – there are claims that it can quell nausea during chemotherapy, relieve glaucoma and stifle the pain of multiple sclerosis – but smoking marijuana also imposes a price.

Last year US researchers showed that squirrel monkeys found the drug addictive, and a Boston team reported that, an hour after inhaling, the risk of heart attack increased fivefold.

Heather Ashton, of the University of Newcastle, reports in the same journal that besides producing severe anxiety, panic, paranoia and psychosis in high doses, cannabis impaired memory and concentration.

There could be heart problems for people with pre-existing cardiac disease, and the drug also suppressed the immune system. Cannabis cigarettes could be as addictive as nicotine, and the tars from cannabis cigarettes contained higher levels of some cancer-causing chemicals than tobacco.

Smoking three or four reefers a day produced the same risk of bronchitis or emphysema as 20 or more cigarettes.

Chronic use might also cause complications in pregnancy and childbirth.

Cannabis will remain illegal, says tsar

The government will reject calls to decriminalise cannabis when it responds to a report on drug policy, the drugs tsar, Keith Hellawell, said today.

His statement comes as a blow to supporters of drugs law reform, who had been hoping for a government about-turn on the issue in the wake of the report, published early last year.

The result of a two-year inquiry sponsored by the Police Foundation and chaired by Dame Ruth Runciman, the report called for a cut in penalties for cannabis, ecstasy and LSD.

Dame Ruth today repeated her warning that the government could not afford to ignore the debate over drugs. 'Our drug laws need some review after 30 years to make them more accurate, more enforceable and fairer,' she said.

'I don't see how in the end they [the government] can avoid joining in what should be a commonsense, undogmatic and constructive debate'

'I don't see how in the end they [the government] can avoid joining in what should be a commonsense, undogmatic and constructive debate.'

Penalties had to be proportionate to the risk of the drug, she told the BBC Radio 4 *Today* programme.

Persistent offenders should end up with a criminal record but those caught with cannabis for personal use for the first time should just receive a caution, she added.

However Mr Hellawell, who has been asked to examine the report, insisted the law would not change.

He has been joined by the home secretary.

'We don't agree with their proposals for cannabis because that would actually amount to the effective decriminalisation of cannabis,' Mr Straw said.

Straw warns against relaxing drug laws

**By George Jones,
Political Editor**

Jack Straw said yesterday that he would welcome a debate on the legalisation of cannabis but held out little prospect that the Government was ready to relax the law on possession of soft drugs.

The Home Secretary promised that medical use of cannabis compounds to alleviate the suffering of those with conditions such as multiple sclerosis would be legalised if trials currently under way showed it to be effective.

But he warned that scientific factors about the effects of cannabis should be borne in mind when considering decriminalising its use. His comments came after an eighth member of the shadow cabinet, Tim Yeo, the agriculture spokesman, admitted having smoked – and enjoyed – cannabis.

He angered the Tory leadership with his admission. It caused fresh embarrassment at a time when party managers had hoped to defuse the controversy caused by the zero tolerance policy on drug possession announced by Ann Widdecombe last week. Mr Yeo said: 'It can be much pleasanter than having too much to drink.'

Seven other members of the shadow cabinet – Peter Ainsworth, Francis Maude, Lord Strathclyde, Bernard Jenkin, David Willets, Archie Norman and Oliver Letwin – have admitted to experimenting with the drug but Mr Yeo was the only one to have said he enjoyed it.

Mr Straw, who has taken a hard line against legalising cannabis, said he had never used the drug. His son William was cautioned in 1998 for selling cannabis to an undercover journalist. He said the row over Miss Widdecombe's plan for £100 fines for possession of even a small amount of cannabis showed the Conservatives were unfit to govern.

He described her proposals as 'mad' because they did not recognise the proportionate damage caused by different illegal drugs. He told BBC Radio 4's *Today* programme that cannabis could have very severe short-term and long-term effects.

'The long-term effects include a very severe exacerbation of mental illness and also include cancer. It is reckoned that cannabis is between two and four times as carcinogenic as tobacco.'

'I am a hardliner on drugs. I think cannabis leads to use of other drugs and I am against that'

Legalisation of cannabis would mean the consumption of a harmful drug would increase and people would then ask: 'Why have you done this? It has made us more unhealthy.'

John Prescott, the Deputy Prime Minister, said yesterday: 'I am a hardliner on drugs. I think cannabis leads to use of other drugs and I am against that.'

During a visit to Peckham, south London, an area that has suffered drug problems, he said: 'I have seen what it does, both in my 10 years at sea and on the estates in my constituency, so I am not very tolerant of that.'

The Government came under pressure from its backbenchers to hold a 'grown-up debate' about the legalisation of cannabis. Martin Salter, Reading West, said there should be a Royal Commission on how resources were allocated to fight drug abuse. He said: 'I would rather have a drugs policy looking at drugs that kill rather than criminalising 6,000,000 people who use cannabis.'

Paul Flynn, Newport West, who has long campaigned for a more liberal approach to cannabis, said he despaired of the Government's attitude. 'Public opinion is ahead of the political cowardice that has been shown by Labour ministers. MPs who tell the truth about drugs are the ones who will have respect,' he told BBC Radio 4's *The World at One* programme.

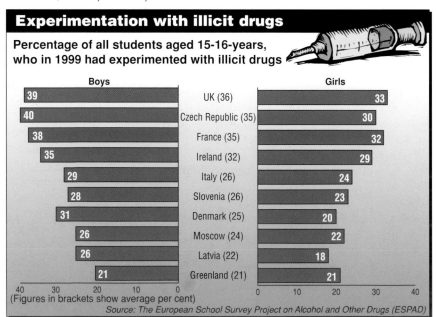

Experimentation with illicit drugs

Percentage of all students aged 15-16-years, who in 1999 had experimented with illicit drugs

	Boys		Girls
UK (36)	39		33
Czech Republic (35)	40		30
France (35)	38		32
Ireland (32)	35		29
Italy (26)	29		24
Slovenia (26)	28		23
Denmark (25)	31		20
Moscow (24)	26		22
Latvia (22)	26		18
Greenland (21)	21		21

(Figures in brackets show average per cent)

Source: The European School Survey Project on Alcohol and Other Drugs (ESPAD)

Jail us or leave us alone, say cannabis users

By Anthony Browne

Cannabis activists are asking to be prosecuted for possession of the drug in an extraordinary bid to break down the laws on prohibition.

The move follows a wave of optimism in the cannabis legalisation movement, which supporters see as akin to the civil rights campaigns that led to the legalisation of homosexuality and women's right to vote.

For the first time in Britain, cannabis campaigners will stand in a general election, fielding up to 100 candidates.

The police and Crown Prosecution Service have become increasingly unwilling to prosecute for possession of cannabis. Juries now routinely acquit users who plead innocent on the grounds of medical necessity. Rather than take people to court, police are issuing cautions, which last week the Government announced would no longer mean carrying a criminal record for life.

However, activists are demanding to be prosecuted so that they can plead innocent under the new Human Rights Act, which prevents the Government from unduly interfering in the private life of an individual. There are at least half a dozen cases going through the courts where activists have refused cautions and deliberately admitted to using cannabis in order to test the Act. They are confident of victory.

Neil Morgan, a cannabis user in south Wales, is being prosecuted for possession after resisting an attempt by police to drop the case. He said: 'Going to court is a golden opportunity – it's the only way we'll change anything. We've waited a long time for this.'

The civil rights group Liberty is supporting the case of Jerry Ham, the founder of a homeless charity who is facing prosecution for possession of 3g of the drug. When he was caught by police, Mo Mow-lam, the Cabinet Minister in charge of drug enforcement, who knew him through his work, phoned him to offer condolences.

Lawyers believe defeat for the Crown Prosecution Service under the Human Rights Act would unravel the drug prohibition laws. The number of CPS prosecutions for possession of cannabis has dropped dramatically, prompting campaigners to accuse it of trying to avoid defeat.

Roger Warren-Evans, a barrister on the council of Liberty, said: 'The Crown Prosecution Service know that, for any simple case, it could provoke a human rights defence. They're backpedalling so they don't get caught with a sucker punch on possession. It would unravel all the rest of the prohibition laws.'

Daniel Westlake, a 21-year-old building labourer, is thought to be the most likely to bring a change in the law. When caught with a small amount of cannabis, he refused to accept a caution and pleaded not guilty under the Human Rights Act. His case is soon to come before the Court of Appeal, which has the power to declare the Misuse of Drugs Act incompatible with the Human Rights Act.

Many police forces have effectively given up enforcing the laws on cannabis possession. Two chief constables, one acting and one retired, have called for its legalisation. A Police Federation report last year called for its decriminalisation, although the Government last week announced it would ignore its recommendations.

As a result, campaigners are becoming increasingly open about using and growing the drug. Colin Davies, founder of the Medical Marijuana Co-operative, is growing plants in Manchester to supply – illegally – more than 100 people with medical conditions. He has been prosecuted three times, and the jury has acquitted him on each occasion. He is now thinking of importing the drug from mainland Europe. 'I think the juries will be just as sympathetic,' he said.

Even social users are openly challenging the police. Mark Gibson, a prospective parliamentary candidate for the Legalise Cannabis Alliance in Cumbria, and a regular user, said: 'There are many more people standing up and being counted. If the police want to arrest me they can, but they don't pay any attention to me any more.' A cannabis rally is being organised in London in May, in full co-operation with the police. A separate march on Downing Street is being planned.

Attitudes have changed dramatically both in the UK and abroad. Last year, a third of the Shadow Cabinet admitted to having tried cannabis. Last month, Belgium legalised the drug, following a similar move by Switzerland last year. Portugal, Spain and Italy have all decriminalised possession of cannabis. Holland has officially tolerated the drug for years.

Warren-Evans says the Human Rights Act would force Britain to follow Europe: 'The cool neutrality of the courts will get the politicians off the hook. That will happen before the end of the year. The whole apparatus of prohibition will fall.'

Cannabis 'to be legal as painkiller in two years'

By Jenny Booth and David Bamber

Cannabis will be legalised for medical use within two years because clinical trials of the drug show it has few side-effects, the chief scientist of the Royal Pharmaceutical Society (RPS) believes.

According to research obtained by the *Telegraph*, the first trial in Britain, on six healthy people, concluded that 'there were no safety concerns' about the drug's use.

Last night Professor Tony Moffat said: 'I have read sufficient in the literature about the small trials that people have already done showing that these are very potent compounds for relaxing muscles, and the anecdotal evidence from MS sufferers who smoke it saying it is absolutely wonderful. All the evidence points that way.' Once accepted as a medicine, cannabis would almost certainly become a social drug too, he added.

Prof Moffat said that cannabis need not take the form of a cigarette with its attendant health risks, and swallowing the drug was not effective as 90 per cent of it was broken down by the liver before having much effect. But a mouth spray or even a suppository would deliver 50 per cent of the drug into the user's system. Medicinal cannabis will not give people a drug-induced 'high' but will be used as a painkiller and relaxant.

Alan Milburn, the Health Secretary, and his predecessor Frank Dobson, have both said the Government would legalise the medical use of cannabis if trials showed a clear benefit. The debate about legalising cannabis for medical use was reignited in 1998 when the House of Lords science and technology committee acknowledged that part of the cannabis plant seemed to alleviate asthma as effectively as conventional treatments.

The RPS is monitoring two large clinical trials of cannabis: a £400,000 study involving 300 patients to see if

cannabis tablets can replace morphine as a painkiller after surgery, and a £900,000 study of 660 patients with multiple sclerosis. Both are funded by the Medical Research Council. A commercial drugs firm, GM Pharmaceuticals, has commissioned two trials of cannabis extracts delivered in a spray squirted under the tongue. The spray takes effect within two or three minutes, almost as quickly as cannabis inhaled from a cigarette.

A report on the first phase of GM Pharmaceuticals' trials said that cannabis was 'well-tolerated' by volunteers, and there were 'no safety concerns'. The trial volunteers reported feelings of 'light-headedness, awareness of a "high", mellow or happy mood, relaxation and dizziness or unsteadiness' at high doses.

The World Health Organisation has promised to transfer cannabis from schedule one to schedule two of its list of drugs, sanctioning it for medical use worldwide, if clinical trials show it is useful as a medicine.

Mike Goodman, the director of the drug charity Release, predicted that cannabis would be decriminalised within five to 10 years and fully legalised within 15. It would be sold either as resin or grass and ready-rolled in packets of five or 10 joints with brand names such as Double Zero, Purple Haze and Northern Lights. Like tar and nicotine in cigarettes, the amount of cannabinoids would be controlled.

ADDITIONAL RESOURCES

You might like to contact the following organisations for further information. Due to the increasing cost of postage, many organisations cannot respond to enquiries unless they receive a stamped, addressed envelope.

DrugScope
Waterbridge House
32 -36 Loman Street
London, SE1 0EE
Tel: 020 7928 1211
Fax: 020 7928 1771
E-mail: services@drugscope.org.uk
Web site: www.drugscope.org.uk
DrugScope is the UK's leading centre of expertise on drugs. DrugScope provides authoritative and reliable information on all aspects of drug policies and problems.

European Monitoring Centre for Drugs and Drug Addiction (EMCDDA)
Rua da Cruz de Santa Apolónia 23-25
PT-1149-045 Lisbon
Portugal
Tel: 00 351 21 811 3000
Fax: 00 351 21 813 1711
E-mail: info@emcdda.org
Web site: www.emcdda.org
The EMCDDA was set up to provide the Community and its Member States with 'objective, reliable and comparable information at European level concerning drugs and drug addiction and their consequences'.

The Florence Nightingale Hospital
11-19 Lisson Grove
London, NW1 6SH
Tel: 020 7258 3828
Fax: 020 7724 6827
Web site:
www.florencenightingalehospitals.co.uk
Florence Nightingale Hospitals specialise in the treatment of psychological and emotional problems and addictions, all within their own specialist areas.

Health Education Board for Scotland (HEBS)
Woodburn House
Canaan Lane
Edinburgh, EH10 4SG
Tel: 0131 536 5500
Fax: 0131 536 5501
E-mail: hebsweb@hebs.scot.nhs.uk
Web site: www.hebs.scot.nhs.uk
HEBS was established on 1 April 1991, replacing the Scottish Health Education Group as the national agency for health education in Scotland.

Life for the World Trust
Wakefield Building
Gomm Road
High Wycombe, HP13 7DJ
Tel: 01494 462008
Fax: 01494 446268
E-mail: lfw@cwcom.net
Web site: www.doveuk.com/lfw
Life for the World Trust is a Christian charity committed to excellence in providing recovery from addiction.

Lifeline
101-103 Oldham Street
Manchester, M4 1LW
Tel: 0161 839 2054
Fax: 0161 834 5903
E-mail: mail@lifeline.org.uk
Web site: www.lifeline.org.uk
Lifeline is an organisation that helps people who use drugs and the families of people who use drugs.

Metropolitan Police Service (MPS)
New Scotland Yard
Broadway
London, SW1H 0BG
Tel: 020 7230 1212
Fax: 020 7230 4276
E-mail:
new.scotland.yard@met.police.uk
Web site: www.met.police.uk
The Metropolitan Police Service is possibly the most famous police force in the world. It is by far the largest of the police forces that operate in Greater London.

Mind
Granta House, 15-19 Broadway
Stratford
London, E15 4BQ
Tel: 020 8519 2122
Fax: 020 8522 1725
E-mail: contact@mind.org.uk
Web site: www.mind.org.uk
Mind works for a better life for everyone with experience of mental distress.

National Criminal Intelligence Service (NCIS)
PO Box 8000
London, SW11 5EN
Tel: 020 7230 3637
Web site: www.ncis.gov.uk
Works to provide leadership and excellence in criminal intelligence to combat serious and organised crime.

Release
388 Old Street
London, EC1V 9LT
Tel: 020 7729 9904
Fax: 020 7729 2599
E-mail: info@release.org.uk
Web site: www.release.org.uk
Release provides a range of services dedicated to meeting the health, welfare and legal needs of drugs users and those who live and work with them. Runs a 24-hour helpline on 020 7729 9904. Release produces a range of publications on the legal and health aspects of drug use.

Transform – the campaign for effective drug policy
Easton Business Centre
Felix Road, Easton
Bristol, BS5 0HE
Tel: 0117 941 5810
Fax: 0117 941 5809
E-mail: info@transform-drugs.org.uk
Website: www.transform-drugs.org.uk
Transform is a national organisation seeking to repeal drug prohibition and to replace it with a truly effective system of regulation and control (i.e. the legalisation of all drugs).

INDEX

*****

The Internet has been likened to shopping in a supermarket without aisles. The press of a button on a Web browser can bring up thousands of sites but working your way through them to find what you want can involve long and frustrating on-line searches.

And unfortunately many sites contain inaccurate, misleading or heavily biased information. Our researchers have therefore undertaken an extensive analysis to bring you a selection of quality Web site addresses.

Mind
www.mind.org.uk
This web site has a vast amount of information. Mind's information unit has produced a number of factsheets, information sheets and contact/resource lists. Most of these are now available on-line. Also booklets can be downloaded as PDFs.

Metropolitan Police Service
www.met.police.uk
Click on either Young People and then on Drugs: know the law or Crime Prevention for a range of informative articles. The index button reveals all the articles on the web site – huge. The News button takes you to the Met's 24-Hour News Bureau.

DrugScope
www.drugscope.org.uk
This site provides objective, accurate and current information on all aspects of drug misuse for professionals, policy makers and researchers. A useful starting point for student research on drug-related issues.

Health Education Board for Scotland (HEBS)
www.hebs.scot.nhs.uk
A very informative site looking at all aspects of drugs, their long- and short-term effects.

Release
www.release.org.uk
A lot of in-depth drug facts can be found on this web site.

ACKNOWLEDGEMENTS

The publisher is grateful for permission to reproduce the following material.

While every care has been taken to trace and acknowledge copyright, the publisher tenders its apology for any accidental infringement or where copyright has proved untraceable. The publisher would be pleased to come to a suitable arrangement in any such case with the rightful owner.

Chapter One: Illegal Drugs

The facts of drugs, © Health Education Board for Scotland (HEBS), *Cannabis*, © Libra Project, *Solvents*, © Release, *Drug use among children rises to 11%*, © Guardian Newspapers Limited, 2000, *The state of the drugs problem in the European Union*, © European Monitoring Centre for Drugs and Drug Addiction (EMCDDA), *How Europe compares*, © The European School Survey Project on Alcohol and Other Drugs (ESPAD), *Drug-related deaths*, © Crown copyright is reproduced with the permission of the Controller of Her Majesty's Stationery Office, *Confident kids likely to try drugs*, © Guardian Newspapers Limited, 2000, *Last use of drugs*, © Schools Health Education Unit (SHEU), *The psychological effects of street drugs*, © Mind, *More than 80% of street beggars are taking drugs*, © Telegraph Group Limited, London 2000, *Drug misuse*, © The Florence Nightingale Hospitals, *Public attitudes*, © The Police Foundation, *Myths about young people and drugs*, © Lifeline, *Drugs homework at primary school*, © Telegraph Group Limited, London 2000, *Drug safety – the basics*, © DrugScope, *Seven in 10 offenders test positive for drugs*, © Guardian Newspapers Limited, 2001, *Drug trafficking*, © National Criminal Intelligence Service (NCIS), *Drug related deaths*, © Crown copyright is reproduced with the permission of the Controller of Her Majesty's Stationery Office, *Drugs tsar hails new detector*, © Guardian Newspapers Limited, 2000, *Getting into trouble with drugs*, © DrugScope, *Seizures of controlled drugs*, © Crown copyright is reproduced with the permission of the Controller of Her Majesty's Stationery Office, *Crack down on drugs*, © Metropolitan Police Service (MPS).

Chapter Two: The Legalisation Debate

High time for a decent debate, © Guardian Newspapers Limited, 2000, *Cannabis research: a story of highs and lows*, © Guardian Newspapers Limited, 2000, *Majority regard cannabis as no worse than drink*, © Guardian Newspapers Limited, 2000, *Ten reasons to legalise drugs*, © Transform, *Belgium legalises personal pot use*, © Guardian Newspapers Limited, 2000, *Don't make a hash of your life*, © Life for the World Trust, *Improving the quality of the cannabis debate*, © British Medical Journal (BMJ), *Cannabis use*, © Crown copyright is reproduced with the permission of the Controller of Her Majesty's Stationery Office, *Scientists list mental risks from smoking cannabis*, © Guardian Newspapers Limited, 2000, *Cannabis will remain illegal, says tsar*, © Guardian Newspapers Limited, 2000, *Straw warns against relaxing drug laws*, © Telegraph Group Limited, London 2001, *Experimentation with illicit drugs*, © The European School Survey Project on Alcohol and Other Drugs (ESPAD), *Jail us or leave us alone, say cannabis users*, © Guardian Newspapers Limited, 2000, *Cannabis 'to be legal as painkiller in two years'*, © Telegraph Group Limited, London 2001.

Photographs and illustrations:

Pages 1, 14, 19, 28, 40: Pumpkin House, pages 11, 17, 21, 27, 31, 34, Simon Kneebone

Craig Donnellan
Cambridge
April, 2001